Laugh

For the

Health

Of It!

(Laughter is another Bandage!)

Carol Dean Schreiner

Laugh for the Health of It

Praise for Carol Dean Schreiner

♥ She's the funniest grandmother I have.
A granddaughter

♥ My little sister giggle every time Cha Cha tickles her. *A grandson*

♥ She's funny! Really funny! *A grandson*

♥ She makes me laugh every time we watch a funny movie! *A granddaughter.*

♥ We've been laughing at her ever since she was born. *Her brother*

♥ We all laugh at her every time she gets into the pool for exercise. *Her pool pals*

♥ She's always made people laugh just looking at her. *Her old neighborhood gang*

♥ She was so funny back in high school she got the Apple Polisher's award for telling the teacher jokes. *Her high school friend(?)*

♥ She's one of the funniest sisters that I have. *Her only sister*

♥ She's not only funny but she's weird. *A son-in-law*

Other Books by

Carol Dean Schreiner

Wonder Woman Doesn't Live Here Anymore

Other Books by
Suellen Brown Miller and
Carol Dean Schreiner

Steps To Storytelling

Laugh for the Health of It.

Copyright June 1999.

Printed in the United States of America.

Design work by Fisher Graphics.

Author's
Photograph by John Trammel

Library of Congress Cataloging 99-094563

Published by Hayter House of Publishers

ISBN 0-9644074-4-2

For information contact
C.D. Communications,
Box 5223,
Norman, OK 73070-5223

Dedication

Dedicated: to people who like to laugh.

Dedicated: to teachers in the classroom and in life!

Dedicated: to my family for having such a delightful sense of humor.
They each had a wonderful knack of story and joke telling. Just listening to them was a great education in the field of humor!

Forward

Not only is laughter a gift, but it is an emotion that can heal. One of my most vivid memories is of spending the night with my grandparents and watching the Red Skeleton show on television. Of course I laughed at his antics. It was impossible not to laugh. But the pleasure I derived came from my grandfather, Chris Shero, as well. Watching him slap his leg in delight and repeat the old, worn-out jokes during the commercials was even better. I loved Red Skelton, but I loved my Grampy even more.

In this book, Carol Dean's willingness to share her humor with us is as generous as Mr. Skelton was in sharing his genius for joy.

As a writer, myself, I know the value of capturing emotions, whatever they be. And while my skills fall into another genre, that of romantic suspense, I still regard the gift of writing as one that should be shared.

So lean back, take a deep breath. The read through the pages of this book is not unlike that of a ride through a carnival fun house- a lot of fun and exhilaration - and a sure cure for the blues.

Sharon Sala
Author of Remember Me,
Touchstone

Acknowledgments

Thanks: to my audiences, who have laughed and then asked, "Help me learn how to use humor." Especially to Floyd Cox, and all the staff and members of the Oklahoma Education Association.

To all the schools who hired me to help teach laughter. Special thanks to the teachers who sat on the floor or stood to hear me. I am deeply honored to have spoken to you.

A Special Thanks to my prayer partners who have prayed overtime to keep my inspiration coming, and my laughter plentiful.

Thanks to Bonnie Eidt for everything from food to editing to suggestions and everything in between.

Thanks to Gwen Marshall from Baptist Integris Hospital for the interview.

Thanks to Dr. Chris Codding of the Orthopaedic and Reconstructive Center in Oklahoma City for her input about her patients and the benefits of laughter.

Thanks to Karla Tolson of the Parkinson Disease Information and Referral Center at Hillcrest 55+, Tulsa, Oklahoma for sharing her stories of healing and laughter.

Thanks to my good friends EJ Phillips and Suellen Brown for their input, encouragement and interest in the book being a good joke book.

Special thanks to all my family for their unconditional love and support and belief.

Thanks to my God for having a beautiful sense of humor.

Thanks for good, honest, healthy laughter that produces miracles!

Contents
Section I

Chapter **Page**

Humor is comical or amusing, either jokes, funny happenings, stories or short lines.

Because it is a safe emotion to use, it's therapeutic, promotes healing, reduces stress, stimulates alertness, improves listening and retains information.

To emphasize a point in the speech, to use as an example, to make the humor have a purpose. Gives you an idea of how stories and jokes are told, to jolt your memory of things that have happened to you that could be used in your speeches.

Wherever you have been too serious or too technical and your audience needs a jolt to awaken. How to present funny happenings in a serious topic. Use "I" stories. How to personalize stories. Pace humor, be brief! Practice telling stories until you know them inside and out.

Chapter	Page

Section II
Jokes

Section III

Introduction

Do you want to be healthier? If someone told you to take a pill daily to be healthier would you take it? How about if someone told you to read or tell a joke daily to be healthier? Would you do it? Often pills have side effects. There are no side-effects with laughter. It isn't even fattening. And it often causes a twinkle in the eye. It's often exactly what the doctor ordered.

Of all the things you do for yourself, one of the most beneficial is to laugh daily! Besides promoting health, it is one of the ways to survive life! Laugh your way through it! It is often the positive attitude that allows you to enjoy the good things in life. Laughing at adversity helps create inner peace and the success to overcome daily problems. Sometimes laughing not only takes the pain away it gets the mind off the seriousness of the situation. Success often means inner peace; the happiness money cannot buy. Peace from within is to know life is good; no matter how bad things can be, there is something good out there. Happiness is an inside job!

People with a sense of humor who can laugh at life will go far in this world because they have imagination. They can see the humor in everyday situations with a successful attitude. Their success can be measured in many ways: in business, in relationships, and most often, most noticeably, in their inner happiness. Often it is the attitude of humor that carries people over, or through, their problems. Abraham Lincoln was often chastised for his humor, but he stated humor was what allowed him to go beyond the pain of his work. Once during a debate with Stephen Douglas, Mr. Douglas called Lincoln two-faced. Lincoln replied, "Now, Mr. Douglas, do you think if I were two-faced, I'd be wearing this one?"

Laughter comes easily to some people. To others it is not easy. Some people need to make a conscious effort to look for humorous happenings and incidents. If we work at looking and finding humor in our lives, we will connect our mind to our Funnybone, so try it. There are two different types of laughter.

One is laughing at ourselves, and the other one is laughing at others. Most of us remember the chant, "Sticks and stones may break my bones but words will never hurt me." That is not true, as words break many of our 'self-esteem bones'. Let's use the good words and do not brow beat people by laughing at them. We try to be too serious, or we think we can laugh at the expense of others. That is not the way. Laughing at others causes damaging low self-esteem to the person receiving that laughter. Positive and successful people don't do it! Of course there are comedians who always put others down. Do you remember Don Rickles who was famous for that type of humor? People who find their laughs by putting someone else down are usually products of low self-esteem themselves. They often want company in their pity party. Some people are so jealous of others they cannot stand to see someone else happy or making something good out of his/her life. Be extremely careful you are not guilty of laughing at someone.

According to statistics the number one fear is Fear of Public Speaking, the #2 fear is of death. After visiting with many people, I have come to believe the #3 fear is death while public speaking. Maybe, the #4 fear is bombing while trying to be funny.

Many times I wrap up a day long meeting with a humorous speech. The attendees have been listening to programs that are full of red-tape regulations, legalese matters, instructions on how to fill out new forms for the company. These topics are necessary but not altogether interesting. So when I talk to them about humor, injecting many humorous stories, they are more than ready for it. I wish some of the other presenters would learn to inject just a little humor. It could help their audience become better listeners.

The very first time I presented this topic to the Oklahoma Education Association the room was so packed that people were sitting almost on my toes. Before the session started a gentleman on the front row said, "I hope you don't spit when you talk." I responded, "I hope I don't either." (Talk about being put under pressure or stress!)

If you ever need to be in front of an audience, whether you are a teacher, preacher, group leader, meeting presider, or public official, there is a time and place for humor. Maybe some of these ideas could help you include more humor in your presentations.

You may not be a speaker or even want to become a speaker. You may only want to learn to tell jokes for the sake of telling a joke. That is great too. Too many people don't really ever learn. Or they are afraid that they will not tell them correctly so don't even try. Take the information from this book and practice telling your jokes to every fence post you see until you get them down good enough to practice on family and friends. You could become the life of the party.

Also, don't stop people from telling a joke just because you have either heard it or heard one similar. It is amazing how often I hear a joke that is similar but has a different twist on the end. We hear the same song over and over so we can listen to a joke over and over. I had an uncle who was a great joke teller. His wife laughed every time she heard his jokes even though I know she had heard them numerous times. That took talent but a great talent it was.

In putting together the jokes, I tried my best to put the jokes into categories to help you find the right joke for your next presentation. However, some of the jokes could fit into several different categories or no particular one. Just enjoy, use, and of course, laugh!

Whatever the reason you are reading this book, please have a laugh on me!

☺

What Is Humor?   Chapter One

WHAT IS HUMOR?

- Comical Incidents
- Jokes
- Funny happenings
- Stories
- Short lines

W ebster defines humor as, a): that quality that appeals to a sense of the ludicrous or absurdly incongruous, b): the mental faculty of discovering, expressing or appreciating the ludicrous or absurdly incongruous, c): something that is, or designed to be, comical or amusing.

This last definition is the meaning, we, as speakers want to implement in our speeches. We can use humor by telling jokes, using funny happenings, stories, or short lines that can provoke laughter. Laughter is a great way to bond your audience together. How many of you can recall a humorous situation when all you had to do was call a certain someone, say a word or two, to have both of you laughing about that situation?

People are always mispronouncing my last name. I tell them, "It's pronounced Schreiner just like the circus. In fact I have five children and believe me it has been a circus!" My kids were so involved that I became the ring master and a master juggler. There were football, basketball, baseball, little league, girl scouts, boy scouts, 4-H, FFA, FHA. They were all in the band. They all took piano lessons. There were voice lessons, speech lessons, drama lessons, flag-team, twirlers, cheer leaders. Do you have any idea how many ball games, concerts, parent-teachers conferences I have attended? My oldest child started college the year my baby started first grade. I had 24 years of having someone in school, and that's not counting college! So believe me I know how to discuss finding humor daily!

Give yourself a laughter test daily. Have you laughed today? What will you do to make certain you laugh? (Have a plan.) What type of things do you consider funny?

When is the last time you had a hearty laugh? What brought it about? Keep a journal of things you consider funny. Write down the funniest things that happen each day.

A speaker should use clean, respectable, tasteful humor. The humor should not be racist or ethnic. Be extremely careful in telling jokes that make fun of someone in particular. You will not know everyone in your audience, and you cannot take the chance of offending one of them by telling personally targeted jokes i.e. fat, "dumb blond," short, physical or mental disabilities jokes. You may talk about yourself, but don't poke fun at some type of person, unless you are making a point. Even then, you are walking on eggshells. Be aware, if using accents or dialects, that you are not making fun or degrading someone.

A hospital committee was once interviewing me before they decided to hire me for a workshop. During the interview they asked if I knew any medical jokes. I told them one about a Jewish couple but I did not want to offend any person. Upon hearing it, they assured me the joke was great and to use it because they had people from many races, religions, and nationalities.

This is the joke: A Jewish wife greeted her husband home from the doctor and immediately asked what the doctor said. The Jewish gentleman replied, "He said not to worry, but I have herpes." His wife asked, "What is herpes?" Since neither knew what it was, she looked it up in the dictionary. Relieved, she exclaimed, "The doctor is right. No need to worry. Herpes is a disease of the gentiles."

After the workshop, one of the participants insisted on walking me to my car, saying the neighborhood wasn't safe. When we almost reached the car he asked, "Carol, would you mind explaining that Jewish joke? I didn't get it." So be extremely careful telling jokes you might have to explain.

Humor is different to different people. As in likes and dislikes, some people like the type of humor we call slapstick comedy. Others can't stand that type or style of humor. Determine the type of humor with which you are the most comfortable in delivering. Realize you will not reach or connect with all of your audience. (You will reach only some of them.) Experiment with different types of humor until you find your style. You can use several different styles, but you have to be comfortable with the style or it will not work. Notice how other speakers use humor. Some people have a dry sense of humor. Some use a sarcastic style. Make a list of the different types to see which ones fit your personality. It needs to be as natural as possible.

☺

WHY DO WE WANT TO USE HUMOR?
Chapter 2

WHY DO WE WANT TO USE HUMOR?
- A. It is a safe emotion
- B. It is therapeutic
  1. Promotes Healing
  2. Produces Endorphins
- C. Humor reduces stress
  1. Helps people look at problems differently
  2. Helps people forget problems
  3. Is relaxing
- D. Stimulates alertness
  1. Improves listening
  2. Improves retention of information
  3. Creates awareness
- E. Bonds people together
- F. Relates you are not alone
- G. Creates Energy
- I. Raises morale

W hy create laughter? We relate with people in three different ways, physically, emotionally and intelligently. We learn through emotion or by repetition. Which of the following emotions do you want to see on the faces of your audience?

Anger	Passion	Repulsion	Sadness
Pain	Happiness	Resentment	Fear
Jealousy	Bitterness	Sensuality	Defeat
Prejudice	Melodrama	Sentiment	Humor

Laughter is the safest emotion to use, but sometimes the hardest, and the least used. You may have heard the question the new speaker asked of a veteran speaker, "Should I use humor in my speech?" The response, "Only if you want to be paid!" The speakers who effectively use humor are often the most sought-after speakers.

So much has been written today about the positive benefits of laughter. In Norman Cousins' book, _Anatomy of an Illness_ he stated when we laugh it releases Endorphins. That is the closest thing to morphine our body produces. Mr. Cousins wrote when we laugh, it is as if we were giving our body an internal massage. Doesn't everyone enjoy a massage? I used to go to a man, a masseur, but now I go to a woman, masseuse. She even comes to my home with her massage table. When she finishes I can roll into the bed and she can lock the door on her way out. Besides, it really gripped my soul to have to pay a man to work on my body!

Mr. Cousins stated in his book he rented funny movies. He laughed enough to heal himself of a crippling spine disease. He stated when he laughed for an hour he could be without pain or pain medication for an hour.

What types of books, television, or movies control your life? Do your choices help you relax, or cause you more tension? Are they a healthy form of entertainment or personal enhancer? Write down some of the ones you have read or watched lately then decide in which category they fit.

Cheerful disposition protects health and prolongs life. Dr. William Fry of Stanford University states when we laugh we release a hormone called Catecholamine. It enhances the blood flow that speeds healing, stimulates alertness, promotes immunity and reduces stress. Therefore, laughing releases Endorphins and Catecholamine, two great chemicals our bodies make just because we laugh. Can you afford not to laugh, not to create these wonderful miracles?

Why laugh? Laughter relaxes the members of your audience enough for them to learn and retain more information, and to enjoy themselves. Can you think of a time when you knew laughter helped relieve tension in your life? Go back in your memory to think of the times when you laughed so much your side, or maybe your jaws, hurt. Have you ever carried something heavy and became tickled? What happened? You became so relaxed your muscles could not carry the load. You had to set down that piece of furniture, box, or whatever. That proved laughter is relaxing.

How many of you have laughed until you cried? Have you laughed so much the tears ran down your checks, and you could barely breathe? I used to have these spells especially when I was a little tickled and tired. The first time my step-granddaughter saw me laugh this much she asked my daughter, "Shari, what kind of drugs does your mother take?" Shari told her I don't take drugs. Amy responded, "Shari, I saw her and that kind of laughing is not normal." Shari told her I was just tired and I would come out of it after awhile.

Ever since then, if I ever laughed a little around Amy she would ask, "Cha-Cha, how tired are you? If you are going to have one of those spells I'm leaving." And do you know what? I don't have many of those spells since my kids have left home. Wonder what on earth brought on the tensions!

Laughter is a great reducer of stress. When my daughter, Shari, was 5 years old, her daddy decided we could make a lot of money by raising chinchillas. We raised the critters but didn't make any money. One Sunday, I had invited my in-laws over for dinner. We were all seated around this big oblong table when Shari asked, "Grandpa, do you know how to tell the difference between a girl and boy chinchilla?" . . . I didn't know what she knew. She was not sitting close enough for me to ram my fist down her throat. She continued, "You lift the tail, If it's a boy it's a male. If it's a girl, it's a female!" . . . I don't know who was the most relieved, my in-laws or me. (This is great when talking about stress.)

There are four natural tranquilizers: exercise, laughter, sex, and music (depends on your age which music you consider tranquil).

I heard a group of college students took identical potted plants placing half of them in a room where hard rock music was played and the other half in a room where classical music was played. The hard rock music plants died. The classical music flowers thrived; doubled the amount of blossoms and the root structure took off like crazy. I'm almost afraid to listen to classical music anymore. I'm afraid what part of me might spread or grow.

Many doctors state exercise also produces Endorphins. Believe me, if you saw me exercise you would laugh enough to release lots of Endorphins. I joined an aerobic class one time. By the time I finished tugging, twisting, and pulling to get my leotards on, the class was over.

Find an exercise partner. Find someone you will enjoy being with, maybe someone you can practice telling your stories to. While you are exercising you will visit, tell stories, laugh, which will make the time go by much faster.

Besides if you release Endorphins by exercising and by laughing you will become twice as healthy.

One woman kept hounding her husband to lose weight and to get some exercise. Finally, he agreed to begin an exercise program. She bought him a jogging outfit and announced she even found him a partner. On that first morning as he was tying his shoelaces, there was a knock on the door. Upon opening the door he found a gorgeous gal who said, "Hi, I'm your jogging partner. Your wife says if you catch me, you can have me." And she took off running fast. For six weeks the man ran hard as he could to catch the young woman. He was getting in better shape every day and calculated he would soon be able to catch her. The morning came and he was ready and waiting when the knock sounded. He opened the door and found a big man standing there, who said, "Hi, I'm your new jogging partner. Your wife said if I catch you I can have you!"

One day I was having lunch with a drug pusher. Well, okay, a pharmaceutical rep. Got your attention, though, didn't I? I thought he might have some samples of medicine in the trunk of his car. I asked him what was the best thing on the market for arthritis since I have a little in my shoulder. He puts his hand over mine and say, "I'm the best thing for your arthritis." I said, "Wait a minute! I'm talking about pain in my shoulder." He responded, "I'm talking about sex. Maybe you aren't aware when you have sex you release Endorphins, which is the closest thing to morphine that the body makes. In fact, they are encouraging residents of nursing homes to have sex so their pain won't be so bad or they won't ever be aware of it." I want all you inquiring minds to know I had pain when I went to lunch and I had pain when I left.

Then when I was speaking for the Health Care Association in Mississippi that summer I mentioned this incident. Some of the nursing home administrators came up to me later and said, "You told that as a joke. We are required to have locks on our doors in case any of our residents want to have privacy."

I told the story somewhere and one man asked me, "What was the name of that nursing home?" I don't know if he wants to visit there or go live there!

Once in naming the four, I named the first three and my mind went blank! I laughingly stated when I thought of sex I got so excited I forgot the fourth one. I finally remembered the fourth. Some of my audience stated it was so funny I should use it that way often!

Believe me, the only one of the four tranquilizers I will be encouraging you to do with audience participation is laughter!

The Integris Baptist Hospital in Oklahoma City has a one-of-a kind skilled nursing unit where they practice MIRTH (Medical Institute Recovery Through Humor.)

This 20-bed unit started in 1996 when the hospital decided to add a skilled unit and also wanted to add a MIRTH unit. The two were combined and now is being utilized by the patients and the staff with the Good Humor Prescriptions. Most of the patients stay range from 5 days to 2 weeks.

The staff utilizes lots of different volunteers from regular hospital volunteers to clowns to dog therapy. The dogs are trained to help patients in their recovery. There are about 12 different dogs in this project. The patient is always asked before being visited by the dog and owner.

One patient had not responded to any of the therapy and seemed very despondent. However she responded to a dog like one she had once owned. She began laughing at the dogs antics. The little dog was all over her bed, licking her, playing with her, encouraging those pats that most dogs love. The patient and the dog bonded. It was as if she realized that someone cared about her. Maybe in her mind she became a different age in her life. Whatever the reason, the dog was friendly, and the patient responded. In fact the nurses could tell that this was a turning point on her road to recovery.

Jokes are posted in each room daily. Another patient enjoyed the humor so much that when he later was a patient in another part of the hospital, he sent his wife over to collect the daily jokes. He said that he needed them to recovery from his present illness.

They have many books and jokes, several in large prints. They have a library of funny movies, Abbott & Costello, Three Stooges, Laurel and Hardy, Charlie Chaplin plus other funny movies. Throughout the ward there are posters of the funny movie stars.

Sometimes humor opens the door for the patients to begin telling some of their own stories to the nurses. Humor has a bonding effect that allows the nursing staff to help each patient.

The nurses wear different types of smocks with amusing cutouts on them. This part of the hospital has funny/humorous decorations.

Once the staff gave water pistols to all the patients and everyone who wanted to participate was fair game. Some of the staff had the large bazooka guns. Finally an older woman patient said that it wasn't fair. She wanted the big gun. The gun became so heavy for her she had to rest it on the arm of her wheelchair. However, she managed to shoot everyone that went down the hallway. And she was having the time of her life. Just because people get older doesn't mean they don't like to play games, play jokes or have fun.

I remember a gentleman who loved to tell jokes and pull jokes on people. When he had to have a pace-maker someone should have warned the staff of his antics. He learned that if he slapped his leg the pace-maker would set off the heart monitor and the nurses would come running. He thought it a great joke. The staff did not!

I speak to many different medical groups on the benefits of laughter. Often the participants know those benefits, they just need a chance to laugh. They have serious jobs and need the opportunity to release the stress by laughing.

Often times, in fact almost all the time after I speak, someone from my audience shares stories with me.

One time after making a presentation for the Oklahoma Parkinson's Support Group a member shared the following story for me to share with other Parkinson's Groups.

A lady in a nursing home asked a gentleman there to sleep with her. "I don't want anything except someone to hold me while I sleep." He agreed and would come in to her room, lay on the bed with her, hold her in his arms and they would sleep that way. This went on for several weeks. Then one night he didn't come to her room. Two more nights went by without him coming to her room. She looked him up and asked, "Why haven't you been sleeping with me at night?" He confessed that he had started sleeping with another woman resident. She asked, "Why her and not me?" He replied, "Well, she's got Parkinson's."

After speaking for a Cancer Breast Support Group one of the women was telling of buying weights to put in her bra before she got her prosthesis bra. She had been in another state for the surgery and would have to fly home. Just as she was about to go through the metal detector at the airport she thought, "OH, Gosh! What if the lead in my bra sets off the detector? What will I do?" Luckily, it didn't and she didn't have any problems. But you should have seen all the laughter the other women were having with her story.

A few weeks after speaking to the Oklahoma Romance Writers Association I was interviewed on a local radio show. The interviewer told me that the week before he had interviewed one of the romance writers. She happened to see my book on a table and asked him if he had heard me speak. He told her he hadn't but I would be the guest the next week and asked why. She responded, "Oh, I have heard her and she is one of the funniest women I have ever heard. In fact, I laughed so much, I almost laughed till I leaked!"

We never know our audience's reaction, do we?

Karla Tolson, RN Coordinator for Parkinson's Disease Information and Referral Center at Hillcrest 55+ of Tulsa, Oklahoma shared the following stories with me.

Early in my career I worked in CCU as a nurse. One night we admitted an overdose patient. He had taken a large amount of cardiac medication which did a wonderful job of giving him no blood pressure nor heart beat. It took two nurses working continually with all the supportive IV's to keep him going long enough to get some of the medication out of his system. We were getting stressed with the tension and enormity of the job in front of us. One of the treatments with overdose of many medications is to give the patient activated charcoal which as it goes through the system binds with the toxins of the medication and pulls it out of the system. The charcoal goes in black and comes out the same way. In this case we were putting the charcoal through a tube inserted into the patient's stomach via the nose. Charcoal hardens quickly and has to be flushed with water to keep the tube open. In this case we were having to give so much and do so many things at the same time to keep him alive that the tube was getting clogged. I was trying to force it through the syringe and into the tubing. Anyway the next thing I knew the pressure forced the end of the tube to separate from the end of the syringe and both of us nurses (along with everything in the room) got covered with charcoal. The patients' spouse was also in the room. The other nurse and I looked at each other and I immediately broke into laughter. Even though the spouse did not laugh she did have a short diversion of the pressure she was under and knew how hard we were working to keep her husband alive.

When I was first out of nursing school and working my first job, the first death had its humorous points. An older man had come in for some testing. As I made my rounds that night I discovered that he had died. At that facility when someone came into the hospital all the belongings were written on a sheet and then were checked when the person left. In the case of death two employees checked the list if a family member was not available. So far the other patient in the room had not awakened. We were trying to check the clothing in the dark with minimal light. The closet was packed and so I was pulling each piece out one at a time as another employee checked the clothing sheet. About half way through the job, I pulled out the next piece of clothing and the next thing I knew there was a foot and shoe swinging out from the back of the closet through the clothes. Needless to say we both screamed and the other patient wakes up wanting to know what happened and why we screamed. We were both scared and the wild thoughts going our minds. Finally I moved some clothes and found the dead patient's wooden leg hung on the hook in the back of the closet. This story always brings laugh whenever I tell it.

Working with people affected by Parkinson's I remind them how important humor is in helping them deal with the affects of a chronic degenerative disease. I always preface it that humor won't take away the problem just gives them a break and helps deal with the situation. The patients share how much learning to laugh at themselves helps to keep a positive mental attitude.

One lady who has problems with the tremors talks about a family joke she and her daughter have. Her daughters have told her when the medicine no longer works they will tie rags to her hands and let her be a duster. She says every time she has a bad day all one of the daughter's needs to say is something about becoming a duster and they will laugh. Soon she is perked up.

Another lady came to support group one day talking about having increased problem with losing her balance and falling. She commented, "The good Lord just wanted to give me gymnastic abilities I always wanted but have never had." Everyone laughed as she said this.

Another man said he told his wife one day when his tremors were worse than usual that he thought he would go to the hardware store and apply for the job of "paint shaker." Needless to say this has become their inside joke to help on the bad days.

Laughter isn't a cure-all. However, it is a way to help handle difficult situations.

Dr. Chris Codding a board certified Rheumatologist, treats

arthritis patients many of which have chronic pain. She feel benefits of laughter are very important for maintaining a positive attitude in dealing with illness and pain. She believes patients who laugh feel better and have decreased pain. Some studies have shown laughter stimulates the immune system. Patients with arthritis and/or chronic pain can definitely benefit from maintaining a positive attitude. Studies have revealed that patients decreased pain if they have a good attitude. Patients with chronic illnesses have been studied and the results reveal that maintaining a sense of humor relaxes muscles and relieves pain. She further states when you laugh or even smile your body releases endorphins and you feel better. Dr. Codding says she tries to laugh with all patients to help them see the importance of having a good attitude. Dr. Codding practices at the Orthopaedic and Reconstructive Center in Oklahoma City and serves as a medical advisor to the Arthritis Foundation.

When you think of the first great comedians which ones to your mind? Bob Hope, Red Skelton, Lucille Ball, Jack Benny, George Burns, Bud Abbott, Lou Costello, Laurel and Hardy, and Charlie Chaplin are the ones I think about. How many of those comedians lived to an old age and even seemed to be pretty sharp too? Of course, we know that Jack Benny only lived to 39. Maybe humor played an influential part of their healthy or long lives.

Laughter is mentioned in the bible numerous times. "Make a joyful noise unto the Lord." "Serve the Lord with gladness."
☺

WHEN TO USE HUMOR?   CHAPTER 3

WHEN TO USE HUMOR?
- A. To emphasize a point in the speech
- B. To use as an example
- C. To make the humor have a purpose

Humor should be used for a purpose: to use as an example or to emphasize a point in your presentation. There needs to be a reason to use that particular humorous point in that speech. Have a reason for it to be in that place or do not use it. Unless you are a comedian or comedienne, humor should have a definite reason to be in your talk. Don't tell a joke or funny story if it doesn't have a bearing on, and tie into, the rest of the story. Have a flow from point to story.

Remember there is a definite difference between reading and hearing a story or joke. When you are speaking, people see your facial expressions and your gestures. The audience hears the reflections in your voice. If, when reading a story, it doesn't makes sense, try visualizing someone telling you the story.

The more you use humor in your speeches, in your talks, in your life, the more you will notice and find you are using it. Humor grows on the person. After awhile it will become more natural. For some people it has almost always been natural. When you work at it being your way, the more natural it will appear. I am happy to share some of the one-liners, stories, funny happenings I use at different times. True, some of them are jokes you have probably heard before. If you have heard them before, don't stop from reading them again. However, many of the stories are true events that happened to my family, my friends, or to me. I honestly think the funniest things are the real things that happen to each of us.

The purpose of sharing them is two-fold: (1) To give you an idea of how stories and jokes are told, and (2) to jolt your memory of things that have happened to you that could be used in your speeches. Think of things that have happened to you that you could include into some topics where the following stories could fit. You might even jot them down. Look into your life as you read these stories and begin keeping your own journal:

A woman was commenting on how much she admired my red hair and stated, "I wish God had made me a red head." I responded, "My hairdresser is good and performs miracles. However, he is not God!"

People are always asking me how I kept a cheerful attitude in rearing my five children. It's because I learned a long time ago I could say with a smile on my face, "Children, you are going to mind me or I'm going to pinch your head off and roll it right down the middle of the highway." I would keep smiling and they weren't sure just what I might do.

Sometimes there are some people who seem to do anything to ruin your day. Have you ever encountered one of them? One time I needed to have an insurance physical form completed. It was clear to me the nurse did not want to take up the doctor's time with just a physical. She could have played "Mama" from "Throw Mama from the Train." I think she might have been a Marine Drill Sergeant in a former life. Immediately, I was reminded of a story I had heard about such a nurse so I decided to see how much of it I could use. She started by asking, "When is your birthday?" My response was September 14th. She asked, "What year?" I answered, "Every year." With a disgusted look she asked me how tall I was. I told her it depended on whether I was wearing clothes or not. She stated clothes didn't make any difference in height. I told her it did to me. When I'm dressed, I am 5'8." She asked how tall I was undressed. I responded, "About this tall." (I crouched down with my hands together in the position of 6:30 on the clock.) Then she asked me how much I weighed. My response was, "It depends on whether I am wearing my glasses or not." She insisted glasses didn't weigh much, but asked me how much I weighed with my glasses on. I told her but I am not putting it down in black and white nor do I tell my audiences.

Then she asked how much I weighed without my glasses. I told her, "I don't know. I can't see those little numbers." She then asked me if my weight has fluctuated lately. Of course, it has. I am the typical American woman with 10 lbs. off and 10 lbs. on. She then asked, "What is the least you ever weighed?" I told her, "6 lbs. 13 oz." She didn't ever smile, but she also never made me upset. (I was slightly smiling inside and probably outside too.)

One time when my mother was in a hospital, my sister was telling her about our breakfast in a waffle shop earlier that morning. "The waitress came up to us," my sister said, "wearing the biggest smile on her face." My 81 year old mother asked, "Where else did you expect her to wear it?" We laughed heavily. About that time her doctor came into the room saying, "Mrs. Roark, you have a severe case of asthma. Have you ever smoked?" (My father was a pipe smoker and had been dead for 27 years, seven years later Mother married a cigarette smoker. At this time, I think Mother had temporarily forgotten about Daddy.) Mother answered with, "I have never smoked, but my husband smokes those cigarettes. We go riding every Saturday and Sunday afternoon and I ride in the back seat." The doctor looked at us quizzically. I told her there were usually 2-3 couples, with the men riding in the front, and the women in the back. With crossed arms, my mother said, "And the men smoke and smoke, making me cough. I told Ernest not to smoke in the car, and he told me to roll down my window. I have never liked him since!" I am not sure she ever did. We laughed again, the doctor laughing with us. The doctor stated she usually suggests the patient's family rent a VCR and funny movies because they are so healing. She continued , "However, there is more laughter in this room than in the room with the funny movies. In fact, I would like my staff to take their breaks with you. I think your family is weird, but a good weird!"

Mother had a great sense of humor. Often times in the hospital while she was so ill, her humor and wit would keep our thoughts positive. Many times, it would keep us from crying. I remember one time I mentioned to Mother that a gentleman on television was cute. She remarked, "Carol Dean, you are too old for cute.

Go for money AND generosity."

One time when Mother was in the hospital I was dozing in a chair while my brother happened to be standing beside the bed. Mother thought she reached down and pulled up the sheet. Instead she got her gown in her hand and pulled the bottom of her gown up to her neck. My brother was gently trying to take the gown out of her hand and put it back over her. He told her what she had done and what he was trying to do. He then told her about a gentleman walking up and down the halls pushing his IV Rack. My brother said, "And mother he keeps looking in your room and he might see your body without your gown." Mother responded, "Well, maybe he needs to, I think I have a good looking body!" (How's that for an 82 year old.)

During a question and answer session after a Self-Esteem workshop a gentleman asked me if I was ever depressed. I said, "Of course." He then asked if anyone ever saw me depressed. I responded with, "Not many." He then preceded to ask me if I were one of those women who woke up in a good mood. When I answered yes he asked if I ever wake up grouchy. I responded, "Of course not. I always let him sleep!"

One of my daughters asked me how I was always able to sing or tell a joke at the breakfast table. My answer, "Why, honey, I knew a big ole' yellow school bus was coming to take you off to school for THE DAY!"

Recently after telling this story a woman approached me saying, "My husband has just retired and I sure wish a bus came down our streets for retired husbands."

Smile. It makes people wonder what you are up to! Have you ever met someone in either the hallway or the sidewalk who wasn't crazy about you? Smile and then quickly stop smiling. It will drive them nuts to wonder what you were smiling about! Don't watch much news - it is too depressing. If something happens you should know, someone will tell you. Become a happy, joy-sharing person. How often, when you ask someone how their day has been, they tell you all of the bad things that have gone wrong. Isn't that depressing? So shock people instead of asking how their day has been, start the conversation by saying, "Wow, I have had an incredible wonderful day!" This could certainly narrow down the number of people who come up to say something to you!

When people ask me how I am, I respond with "Wonderful, marvelous, rich and famous, trim and healthy." One day in a store after responding this way another customer said, "And delusional!"

Whenever I hear someone griping a lot I'm reminded of my favorite story of the three bears. The Papa Bear said, "Someone has eaten all of my porridge." The Baby Bear said, "Someone has eaten my porridge too!" The Mamma Bear said, "Gripe, Gripe, gripe, I haven't even poured it yet!"

Laugh every chance you get, because suppressed laughter goes straight to the hips. I certainly don't want to become wider because I didn't want to laugh!

LIFE IS TOO SHORT NOT TO LAUGH -- LIFE IS TOO LONG NOT TO LAUGH. Both ways are right. The Sioux Indians have a wise saying: The first thing people say after death is "Why was I so serious?"

Driving back from a speaking engagement one day, I felt like I was coming down with a cold. I decided that when I got home I would do nothing for the rest of the day. I was really thinking about maybe having a pity party, eating chips and drinking pop! Suddenly out of the blue, a song popped into my mind that changed my feelings. Have you ever tried to have a miserable day while you are humming, "Chitty, Chitty, Bang, Bang?" Now, when I get up feeling a bit tired, I begin singing that song.

After spending a few days sick in bed with the flu I finally was well enough to drive to the beauty shop. I knew I looked terrible so stuck this note to the dash: "If injured in car wreck, please call my hair dresser first."

I heard a motivational speaker say we can be whatever we want to be. She stated we just need to say to ourselves over and over what we want to be and it will happen. All that night I kept saying, "I want to be a size 10. I want to be a size 10." The next morning I was amazed! It worked, but I didn't mean size 10 for my feet!"

While visiting with a magician on a cruise ship I asked him if he could really make things disappear. He said, "Certainly!" "Great," I responded, "please make 10 lbs disappear from my waist and hips."

One day I had a few hours to wait between a keynote and a breakout session, so I went into the hospitality suite to wait. Being the only person in there, I stretched out on a sofa to rest. Then two of the hotel staff came in to refurbish the refreshment. They spoke to me and I stated I was hiding. After they finished their work, one of them approached me. He asked, "Heidi, would you like a Coke?" I have been told I don't always cross my 't's and add my 'g's but now I believe it.

Send flowers to yourself and sign a crazy card about how wonderful you are. Makes people at work raise their eyebrows! Now, if you are married, be careful what you sign on the card, and tell your spouse about it before someone else does! Take a story and embellish it. When attending a convention I realized how handy husbands could be. I particularly noticed it when one piece of my luggage made it to the airport and the other piece of luggage stayed at the hotel. Most of the luggage belonging to couples arrived at the airport intact. A few weeks later I spoke at a single's convention where I saw all types of dating services. There was computer dating, horoscope dating, matchmaking, and escort services. After much deliberating, I bought my own Escort! Everywhere I go, my escort takes me. (After a long pause, I continue.) I bought myself new car! (You would be surprised of how quiet the room becomes for those few seconds.) Isn't that story better than just stating I have a new car? After speaking one day, some of the people who had hired me were helping me load my car. One of the women exclaimed, "You weren't kidding. You really have an Escort!" I asked her why she had not believed me. She said it was such a good line, she figured it was a joke.

Several years ago I was forced to take an early retirement after a 21-year marriage. Sounds much better than the truth that my husband left me for a blond bimbo, 'Thang-ette!'

I was devastated to put it mildly. About 18 months later my cousin, Janet, and I went to have a makeover by Charlie's Angel's makeup artist. While he was applying the makeup he stated, "I can tell by the lines around your eyes you are a fantastic lover. Does your husband know this?" I answered, "I guess not. He left me last year for another woman." He responded with, "Oh, some men!" I laughed and realized I was healing because I could now laugh about the worst thing that had ever happened to me.

Ever notice the difference between men and women's driving habits? When a woman is driving and gets lost, she stops and asks directions. What does a man do when he is driving and gets lost? He keeps on driving. It's really not the men's fault, Moses started it. He wouldn't stop and ask directions either. I have worried lately, though. I have gotten lost and kept driving telling myself, "I'll find my way in a minute." I was scared I was becoming masculine so I quickly got a hormone shot!

Recently, when donating blood, one of the volunteers cautioned us not to do any heavy work like cooking or cleaning. I told her I don't believe in using, or doing, four letter words like cook, bake, wash, iron, dust, DIET! I used to add 'pump' gas. I hated to have the essence of unleaded on me for the day. She thought that was one of the funniest remarks she had ever heard. Every few minutes she would come over to ask me what they were since she kept omitting one of them.

During a luncheon at a large hotel in Dallas, we were served large servings of chocolate cake. Since I had just spoken, I just wasn't up to eating much, so was not going to eat my cake. The gentlemen to my left offered me his cake. When I stated I wasn't going to eat mine, the man to my right suggested I take both pieces of cake home with me. I laughingly said I didn't think it would be proper to take cake from a banquet setting. He asked for the doggie box himself. Then I remembered the following evening I was hosting a small birthday party for my daughter. I realized I really needed six pieces of cake. Two more people at my table gave me their cake, and after the luncheon I found two more people who didn't want their cake. As I was putting these six pieces of cake in the box, the Emcee for my program came up to me. He asked, "What are you doing?" When I explained the situation, he stated, "I have always heard of people walking their talk. But you are the first one I have ever met. You said you didn't use those four letter words and you meant it!" The next day I asked my daughter what type of cake she wanted for the dinner and her response was chocolate. I asked her if it was all right if I didn't make the cake myself. Also, was it okay if I brought it from Texas? She exclaimed, "You bought me a cake in Texas?" Suddenly, she quizzically looked at me. She stated, "You didn't buy it, did you?"

Now, I don't know what on earth makes my children suspicious. Do you? Often people ask me how come I'm not afraid of public speaking. They ask how do I visualize my audience. Others tell me they have been told to picture the audience in their underwear. In doing so, the fear is supposed to be removed from the speaker. Don't believe it! I remember one night at a fund raising event; I met a local TV newscaster. When introduced to him, I stated since I had seen him on TV so often I felt like I knew him. He stated I didn't know it, but a small TV camera was in my TV. While I was watching their news cast, they were watching me in my blue chenille robe. I laughingly said, "That's not me. I'm the woman in the black negligee! Remember that tomorrow night when you are signing off your program."

Discerning age is a tricky business. One time I had met a man at a single's gathering and neither of us knew the other's age. We both assumed we were real close to the same age. I had an inkling I was a little bit older; during the following conversation, I was telling him my 21-year-old daughter had just moved home with me. She didn't want to live by the rules my other two daughters did. (Clue #1) He said, "Wow! You have a 21-year-old daughter. You must have been about 15 when she was born." (Since she wasn't my first born, I didn't know how old I was when she was born. Do any of you know how old you were for your third child?) I stated, "Well, I really don't know how old I was." (Clue #2) He exclaimed,

"YOU DON'T KNOW HOW OLD YOU WERE WHEN YOU HAD A BABY?" After a long pause, I replied, "No, because she is not my oldest child." (Clue #3) You have a child older than 21?" After a longer pause I said, "I have two children older than 21." (Clue #4) With a stunned look on his face he asked, "Just how old is your oldest child?" With the straightest face I have ever had, I said, "He's 28. I was only 12 when he was born." He smiled a little and said, "You are kidding. Aren't you?" I agreed. I finally told him the truth. All that year I learned to say that line extremely well. I almost believed I was only 40!

☺

WHERE AND HOW TO USE HUMOR?
Chapter Four

WHERE TO USE HUMOR
- Wherever you have been too serious
- Whenever you have been too technical

HOW TO USE HUMOR?
- Use "I" Stories
- Personalize your speeches.

How often do we hear pointless jokes, stories or dumb jokes that rob the speaker's time? Those dumb stories also can discredit you as a speaker. How many times have we heard the line, "Something funny happened to me on the way here tonight" but it wasn't funny?

I have heard for several years the average listening span for an audience is 4 minutes, 15 seconds. Most people need a jolt to wake-up, to stimulate their minds so they will continue listening. The mind cannot absorb more than the body can endure! Laughter is frequently that jolt! Besides, if you get into the habit of provoking some humor every few minutes, people might almost doze, and then think, "Hey, it's about time for another funny I don't want to miss."

I am often the speaker at the end of the conference or the day's training. Even though the information presented was necessary and informative, it was sometimes too much data and not enough interesting facts. Attendees come out bored, restless, and tired because they needed some type of entertainment during the presentations. Now, that is not saying the presenters were not good in what they were doing. It just means the information could have been presented with a few humorous comments throughout the presentation to help the audience's attention. We are all entertained through the TV making it harder and harder to stay with factual information.

Often times if we wait long enough, many situations will become laughable. Not everything, but many. I have read that eighty-two percent of the things we worry about never happen. Why waste your time worrying about them?

A recently divorced woman in my divorce support group was commenting on how her ex-husband's telephone calls about their children un-nerved her. She was asking if she would ever get over the trauma of answering those calls. She seemed to become so agitated she couldn't think straight. One of the gentlemen suggested she tell her ex she was busy. Tell him to call her back in 30 minutes. This would give her time to calm down, relax, and think through some of the topics they were to discuss. It would allow her some control of the situation. A second gentleman told her to state she would call back in a certain time frame. This would allow even more control of the situation. She thought they were super ideas. I then suggested in addition to saying she was busy, be gasping for breath, saying, "I can't ... talk . . right .. now, call back .. . . in about . . . .30 minutes." Everybody loved the answer, they laughed, and she commented she wanted to get to the place where I was. Believe me, it didn't come in a few short weeks. It took years of wanting to reduce my stress and have a healthy, happy life!

Use "I" stories. The story will be more believable if you adapt it as a personal one. Use certain people in the audience IF you have checked it out to make certain it will be okay. Most Emcee's, presidents, meeting planners, are okay for those jokes, but they are also used too often. Meet people before hand. Call them by their name.

Make yourself the blunt of the jokes, whenever possible. It takes a big person to admit their faults and whenever you do you will endear yourself to the audience. Just be certain you are healed of the topic before you speak about it. Don't use the chance to vent your anger just because you have the power, or the control.

Pace humor. Have a reason to use the humor to make a

point, not to tell a joke. Many professionals will tell you to sandwich your humor. Point, humor, point.

Be brief. If you use too much of your time getting into the joke, you will have lost the crowd. You might start by learning to use one liners instead of long stories.

Be certain you know the joke, and the punch line. Don't be like the minister who kept losing his congregation's attention. One day he asked another minister how to keep them awake. The older minister stated whenever he thought he might be losing the congregation's attention he would change his voice a little and tell this story. "Last night I found myself in the arms of a woman who wasn't my wife." When he got their attention he would continue, "I found myself in the arms of my dear ole' mother." A few weeks later the young minister noticed the glaze over the eyes of his parishioners. He changed to a high pitched voice and stated, "Last night I found myself in the arms of a woman who wasn't my wife." Every head came up. Every eye focused on him. He nervously blurted out; "I forgot who it was!"

Recently, when I was telling this story at a convention, I allowed a long pause before saying that punch line. One of the women in the audience, either thought I forgot it, or got so caught up in the program she blurted out the line. I looked at her and said, "Please, be quite! It is my joke and I am in control of this meeting!" Everyone laughed even more.

Pauses are extremely important in telling jokes. Sometimes the pause could be before the punch line, or the important word in the punch line. Sometimes pause after the punch line. Pause before something that is out of the ordinary. They are expecting you to say one thing but you say another one instead. And always pause after you finish telling the joke to give the audience enough time to laugh. Don't step on your laugh lines.

Accenting a word is just as important as pauses. Also, make sure you do not drop off your sentence. Many people speak softer at the end of the sentence, or just let the words trail off. When accenting the word you may want to stretch the word out too. In some of the following jokes I have underlined the words that I either stretch or accent to make certain the listeners get that particular word or phrase.

You must be prepared for a joke to bomb at times. Sometimes you could say, "Well, most intelligent people laugh at that line." Point to a spot on your notes, and say, ""Well, here it says to pause for laughter." Others suggestions, "I didn't think it was funny either." Many times you can even make a point of the opposite effect of not being funny. What is funny to one person is not funny to others. Learn how to save the day when the laughter does not come. You might even say, "I won't use his/her jokes anymore." (Or you could use someone in the audience that everyone knows.)

Experiment with pauses and emphasizing the words. Play around with the different ways you can say them. Remember practicing saying sentences with the emphases on a different word each time you say it. Well, do it again. Practice until you become comfortable saying the joke your way. It doesn't have to be the way you heard it but the way you want to deliver it. At least if it is funny that way.

I go by the double name of Carol Dean, and have all of my life. There were several Carol's growing up in my home town of Frederick, Oklahoma, and we each kept our middle name to have an identify. Several of us lived there for a good part of our adult life. One of the women, Carol Lynn, teaches the kids in school. Another one, Carol Rae, teaches piano and voice to the kids. Carol Dean furnished the kids.

So many people asked me if Dean was my maiden name and I go through this long story of the three Carols. One day, after explaining this to a woman, she stated I seemed a little old to be using two names. I laughingly said I guessed it was a southern thing. Then I asked her, "By the way, what is your name?" She answered, "Mary Ann." I then asked, "Is that one or two words?" She responded, "Two, but it is always used together!" And I responded, "And in my household, my two names always go together too!"

I know for sure God is a man. If God was a woman, we women wouldn't go through childbirth! People are always trying to tell me funny people are just born that way. I have given birth FIVE times and birthing is not a laughing matter!

Never argue with idiots. You may discover they're doing the same thing

When visiting in my old hometown people say, "You are looking so good. I guess you have found a man." "No! No! NO!" I answered, "That's why I am looking soooo good!"

When recently asked if I had prayed for a husband, I answered, "Why should I want to tempt the Lord? He answers prayer."

A man traveling across the state stopped in a restaurant for a late lunch. Being the only customer, he was receiving excellent service from a beautiful young waitress. As she placed the ticket beside his plate she asked, "Sir, are you married?" The man got so excited he almost popped the buttons off his shirt & replied, "I was when I left home this morning. What did you have in mind?" She said, "I was hoping you weren't married, because you would be just right for my mom."

Once upon a time, I cooked dinner for my daughter, her boyfriend and my gentleman friend. My daughter, Kristi, and her friend, Richard, were both in college. After dinner, Kristi and Richard went into her room, to study. My friend and I watched TV. Then my friend knocked on Kristi's bedroom door and asked, "Kristi, may I borrow some books? I'd like to take your mother to her room to study."

With my farming background I have the opportunity of speaking to several agricultural associations and related businesses. Most of the people identify with the following true story. My friends, Brooks and Mary, had not been married very long when he asked her to drive the truck. He wanted her to pull the tractor to get it started. Now, Mary didn't know a lot about pulling tractors. She knew in driving in the sand, (where they now lived) one had to drive fast to keep from getting stuck. She didn't want to get a truck and tractor stuck in the sand. Brooks climbed on the Johnny Pop John Deere tractor. He told her when the tractor started he would take off his hat and wave at her. Mary started the truck and kept looking back to see if the tractor was running, but Brooks was holding on. She figured she had to drive faster so she did. When she looked, Brooks was holding on the steering wheel with both hands. She drove even faster but Brooks wasn't waving the hat. He was still holding on. Finally, after driving over a half mile, she slowed down and stopped. When she went back to the tractor she was puzzled to fine it running. She said, "Brooks Bolin, you said when that tractor started you would wave your hat so I could stop." Slowly, he unwrapped his fingers from the steering wheel, and exclaimed, "I couldn't wave my hat because I didn't dare turn loose!"

Several times when I have told that story, someone asked if I had been told that about him or her? I hear other stories extremely similar.

Several years ago, I realized the real version of "T'was the Night" didn't faintly resembled my Christmas Eve. I was always busy with the hustle and bustle of putting together toys, cooking, etceteras, so I decided to write my own version. Which version fits your household?

T'WAS THE NIGHT BEFORE CHRISTMAS
T'was the night before Christmas and all through the hectic Schreiner house.
Not a creature was sleeping, not kids, cats, dogs, or the mouse.
The stockings were hung by the chimney -- all 15 of them.
And my kids were thinking, "Good ole' mom, she'll come through again."
The stereos were blasting back in the rooms with the beds
While visions of Tom Selleck and Vanna White were going
through my darlings' heads.
I was out in the kitchen-- been there all day long,
Cooking and baking and had just put the turkey on,
When out in the den I heard such a clatter,

I ran in there and said, "Now what in the ...heck is the matter?"
Ashes and soot were flying everywhere and Santa fanning his
britches said, "You shouldn't have a fire in there!"
He was the grungiest looking Santa, so skinny and tall.
The beard on his chin was so dirty and on his head he had almost
no hair at all.
A bottle of Jack Daniels I spied in his pack. And I thought,
"He's been in the liquor cabinet instead of eating the little kids'
snacks."
He looked at all the stockings and said "You must be the lady in
the shoe."
Gave me a thorough look-over and said, "I know what you must
like to do."
He started to fill the stockings, stopped and read the list twice.
Exclaimed "Mercedes! Rolex! Lady, you and your kids weren't
that nice!
But I'm tired and I'm hungry and all out of sorts,
If you let me sleep over, I'd feel better, after one little snort.
And then I fill those stockings with silver and gold.."
I said, "Wait a minute, Santa, you're getting just a little too bold!"
He didn't get my message, took one step closer so I throw him out
in the snow!
He staggered to his sleigh, to his team gave a faint whistle.
Their take-off was bumpy, those reindeer looked fizzled.
But I heard him exclaim to his leading reindeer.
"Rudolph, make sure we don't stop HERE NEXT YEAR!
☺

WHERE TO FIND HUMOR   CHAPTER FIVE

WHERE TO FIND HUMOR

- A. Look at your life.
- B. Read joke books.
- C. Watch and listen to others.
- D. Keep a journal daily of the funniest happenings that happen.
- E. Read newspapers & magazines with an eye on humorous stories.

Look in your own household, or your own life. The best stories will be your own stories. When you are using your own stories this usually prevents others from your stories from the platform. Of course, when people do use your stories, it is considered to be a compliment.

When my children were small, with everyone in school except 4 year-old Kristi, she and I went grocery shopping. The manager of the stores placed a piece of bubble gum in her hand. I asked her, "What do you say to the man?" She answered, "What about one for my sisters?"

Use tried and true jokes, especially when first building your material. When you know that several people probably heard it before, give the credit to someone else. Please don't tell people you are going to tell a joke. Just weave it into your speech or your conversation. When you say, "I heard this joke and thought it was funny" it sometimes causes a less-laugh factor. After telling it you might say that was one of your favorite jokes/stories. When telling something as a true story and people know it isn't true, you lose credibility with your audience. They might think if you are not sincere with this story, you might not be sincere with the rest of your presentation.

Clip and keep Reader's Digest and newspapers articles. However, DO NOT use those stories the same month you read them. Most of your audience read them too. Put them in your file for later times.

Keep a journal. Write down funny events that happen every day. Take notes when listening to other people.

Watch people. You will be amazed at how you will spot those funny events and someday will find a place to use them. Most of the times true stories are funnier than anything one could ever make up.

Make a file for humor and as you collect more jokes divide into groups. Ask other people to look for you. Believe me, the more you speak and tell jokes, the more people will come up to you to tell you their jokes.

Look for cartoons that will help emphasize your points. You can talk about them however; YOU CANNOT use them for overhead transparencies or in printed material. You can always read them and be okay with copyright laws. Often the cartoons are exactly what you wanted to say to make your point.

READ JOKE BOOKS DAILY. If you don't have much to laugh about, buy joke books and read them daily. Instead of sending flowers to sick people, send joke books. Rent the funny movies and watch them with someone who laughs easily. Laughter is so contagious. You can't help laugh when you hear someone else laughing. I have a great collection of funny movies that I watch occasionally. Or I watch them when I need a lift. We all need laughter at various times in our lives.

I exercise in the deep water at the "Y's" pool several mornings a week. One morning a little girl, about 6-8 years old, paddled over to me. She asked, "lady, when you were a little girl, did they have swimming pools?" (I should have answered, "Yes and I learned to hold my breath a long time, what about you?")

Two of my grandchildren were spending the night with me when suddenly 2 year old Blair decided she wanted her Momma. Her crying just kept getting louder and louder. I finally told her that if she were crying too loudly we wouldn't hear the doorbell. Then her mother and father couldn't get in. Immediately, she hushed to listen for the doorbell and was asleep within five minutes. I used the same tactics on my children when we would be sitting in the fields during wheat harvest. Some times they would get to arguing and I would ask, "Did you hear those rabbits?" They answered, "no." I continued, "you have to be extra quiet to hear them. Listen! Listen! Did you hear them?" It worked. Of course, that happened when they were very young. And for you city slickers, rabbits don't make loud noises.

I brought back a Sugar Daddy from La Seine River (pronounced La Sin) in Paris. The brand of the sugar packages was 'daddy'. But when I state that first sentence people look at me questionably.

The summer before my son, Kirk's senior year of college he worked in a different part of the state from where we lived. Toward the end of the summer he was driving home to meet his old high school cronies for their last weekend together before they went to their different schools. Suddenly a state trooper stopped him. The officer approached him and said, "Sonny where in the heck do you think you are going and what were you thinking about driving so fast?" Kirk quietly replied, "I was just going home to see Momma!"

After driving in heavy snow for several hours, I arrived at my son's house. I told my 5-year-old granddaughter, Felicia, I might need a nap before we played some games. However, the nap didn't materialize. When her bedtime arrived, she looked at me and said, "Let's go to bed." I explained to her I was going to stay up for a while longer. She looked at me, and exclaimed, "Remember, you never did take your nap."

I purchased a beautiful beaded gown I would wear as Emcee for a beauty pageant. When modeling it, Felicia looked at me and said. "Oh, you are just beautiful!" After this five-year-old granddaughter had given careful consideration about this dress she asked, "But are you still a grandmother?"
I told her I was but I sure didn't feel like it when wearing such a beautiful dress.

During the oil boom in Oklahoma I was attending a women's conference in Oklahoma City. On the elevator with a few other women, there were several businessmen dressed in three-piece suits. I overheard one of the men say, "While we are here, I want to see the men called, "Dirty Necks!" Much to the dismay of my friends I couldn't help snicker. I asked the men if they might mean 'Rough Necks' or Red necks'?" They meant the men who worked on the oil well rigs.

My mother was famous for thinking mentholatum could cure anything. Mother was bedfast and had to always ask others to do things for her. One day her minister was visiting her. Several times she asked him to hand her the mentholatum, to either rub on her nose, her lip, and even her teeth. Finally he told her, "Well, May, I need to go, because I need to finish mowing my yard. My lawnmower quit on me this morning and I need to see if I can get it started again." She replied, "Take this mentholatum because it just might fix it."

My sister, Mother and I were discussing long ago stories. We were re-telling about the time Mother drenched my daddy with the garden hose. She had mistaken him for my sister coming out on the porch. They had been having a water fight. I asked Mother, "What did Daddy do then?" She answered, "Well, I imagine he went in and changed his clothes."

When traveling on Southwest Airlines recently the steward was hilarious. As he was explaining the oxygen mask, he put it over his face and said, "Now breath normally, gasp, gasp, gasp!" Then as we were taking off he talked into the mike in a tranquilizing voice; "You are getting sleepy, very sleepy. You are not thirsty. You are not hungry. You do not want to bother your steward or stewardess on this flight!" ☺

WHO NEEDS TO USE HUMOR?   Chapter Six

Who needs to use humor?

- ♥ Everyone who speaks.
- ♥ Everyone who wants his/her audience to be entertained.
- ♥ Everyone who wants his/her audience to remember the message.

The more I speak to groups and visit with my audiences, I realize love and laughter go together. In the homes where there is an abundance of love, there is laughter. In the homes where there is no laughter there is probably no love. Too many people, children of today and yesterday, are only laughed at, not laughed with. Maybe, this is the one way you can help your children and their friends. Make certain there is good wholesome laughter at your house every day. You might have a joke contest each day, or have everyone tell the funniest thing that happened to him or her that day. The more you think about humor, the more humor you will notice.

The real Funnybone on humans does not make us laugh. In fact, when we accidentally hit it, it hurts, give us a weird feeling. That spot is located close to the humerus bone; thus, it has been named the 'Funnybone.'

The same principle holds true about humor. What is funny to one person is not necessarily funny to someone else. Too often people derive their laughter by laughing at someone else. Many people can recall an incident where you and a friend had a good laugh. You could call that person, talk about the incident and laugh again, right? But how many of us can recall the times where we have been laughed at? The times we have been on the receiving end of jokes or remarks that were not funny to us? We must understand as a human being we have the power to help or to hinder a life. Sometimes, some lives are almost shattered by people using the wrong type of humor.

I heard this story years ago as a true story. I have even read it in other books as it is now considered a universal story. The response I receive when telling it makes me want to share it over and over. In fact, many people tell me to make certain I never stop telling about Timmy. The message is as strong and clear as it was when I first heard it.

This is how I tell it.

I want to share a true story that I read many years ago about a little boy named Timmy who was in Mrs. Thompson's third grade class. You may have heard it or read it but it has so much value that I want to tell it to you again.

The children in Mrs. Thompson's third grade class called Timmy names, "Stupid! Dummy!" Timmy never passed a test, never handed in homework or participated in class.

In desperation Mrs. Thompson went to the second grade teacher to see what type of student he had been in there. She was shocked to learn that he is the same in the third as he was in the second. She exclaimed, "Why on earth did you pass him then?" The second grade teacher stated, "Well I checked with the first grade teacher and she stated that he was her star pupil. However, his mother died at the end of that year and his father was too busy to help Timmy. But someday, some way, someone will unlock the key to his potential and he again will be that star pupil." Mrs. Thompson stated, "I have an over-crowded classroom as it is. I don't have time to give individual attention. Unless he changes, he will not pass my class!"

A few weeks later at the Christmas party the students brought gifts to Mrs. Thompson. The children laughed at Timmy when he came in with his gift wrapped in old used paper stuck together with masking tape. They laughed even more at the party when Mrs. Thompson opened his gift. For there was a bracelet with some stones missing and a bottle of cologne, half-full.

Mrs. Thompson was brilliant. She put on the bracelet, hiding the part with the missing stones. She opened the cologne, took a deep sniff then put some behind her ears and behind the ears of the little girls who were sitting close to her. She exclaimed, "My, how lovely we smell!"

At the end of the party all of the students said, "Merry Christmas and good-bye, Mrs. Thompson" and ran out the door. All except Timmy who had been standing in the far corner. Slowly he made his way up to her chair. He put his hand on the bracelet stating, "I thought Mother's bracelet would be pretty on you." Then he took a deep sniff. "Oh, you smell just like my mother did!" He threw his little arms around her, hugged her tight, and he too ran out the door.

Mrs. Thompson sat there and wept. She had wanted Timmy to change but she had not been willing to make the transitions in her own life to help him.

When the holidays were over and school resumed she took Timmy aside and asked if there was any chance that his dad would allow him to stay after school to help her. That day began his first day of private tutoring. The key to his potential was unlocked and he became the best student she had ever had. He was her star pupil. She hated for school to be over that spring because she hated to lose that daily association she was having with Timmy.

That fall Mrs. Thompson went to the fourth grade room the first day that students arrived to see how Timmy's summer had gone. But Timmy and his dad had moved away and no one seemed to know where.

Nine years went by and Mrs. Thompson received a graduation announcement from several states away with a note. "Hi, this is Timmy. I have just graduated with honors. And I have won a full scholarship to become a medical doctor. I owe it all to you because you taught me to love to study. Love, Timmy."

Eight years later Mrs. Thompson received another graduation announcement. This one was from the medical university with this note: "Hi! This is soon-to-be Dr. Tim. This is your prescription:

Come to my graduation and please stay the next day for my wedding. I am marrying a wonderful girl. We want you to sit where my mother would have sat because you are the closest thing that I have for a Mother. Love, Timmy."

We don't know how many lives Timmy healed, he saved, he touched. We don't know how many Timmies come into our lives everyday. They come in all shapes, sizes, colors, and nationalities. Some people say one person doesn't make a difference. Everyone makes a difference, it is up to each one of us to see what difference we each make.

How many times have we helped ruin someone because we laughed at him or her? Some people can take adversity and laugh right back in its face. Others allow that adversity to ruin their day, their feelings, their self-esteem, possibly their lives. Can we take a chance on what it will do to another person to laugh at them? Can you think of times when people laughed at you and it hurt? Are the scars still there? One person can always make a difference. What kind of difference do you want to make?

I love to wear hats. One day I was trying on a hat that had a feather in it. The feather was so long and tall that nobody would be able to sit behind me in church. I was contemplating on whether to buy the hat or not when I noticed a woman coming down the walkway in the mall. She looked as if she had the weight of the world on her shoulders as she walked slowly down that walkway with a frown a mile long on her face. We made eye contact and I motioned to the hat. I offered her a thumb's up or a thumb's down. She surveyed the hat and slowly gave me a thumb's up. While she was doing this her shoulders lifted allowing the world to fall off. She put some spirit in her walk. And her frown was replaced by a big smile. In fact, she smiled so much that I did not buy that hat!

After the Timmy story, I immediately tell my hat story. This changes the emotion and gets people to laughing. In the movie *Steel Magnolias* the women are crying when leaving the cemetery. The mother of the deceased young woman says she is so mad that she wants to hit someone. Suddenly one of the women grabs the older woman and says, "Here, hit her!" Instantly everyone in the audience starts laughing when they were crying minutes before.

I want those same results. I want people to feel the sadness and the emotion of sadness but not to dwell and stay there. It depends on the purpose of your story and how you want to leave your audience.

When I published my book, "Wonder Woman Doesn't Live Here Anymore" I sent one to a man in my hometown that had encouraged me in the speaking business. He called to tell me how extremely proud he was of me. Then he stated that he wanted to order five books. He said that he would pay for them. He wanted to give them to the five people in Frederick who laughed at me. People who laughed at me behind my back when I said that I was going to become a professional speaker. Now, that got me down for at least 30 seconds. I wasn't surprised, but I had never heard it spoken before. I told him, I would mail him the books, and the bill. I just wanted to know the names of those five people! And they better not all be relatives!

In speaking to the IRS recently I went over the terms of my contract with them. (1.) I would never be audited again (they laughed and guess who got audited the next year.) (2.) That speech could be counted as a big contribution. (They laughed more.) (3.) That they would send their five meanest auditors to Frederick to a list I recommended. Guess what five would lead the list?

POINTS TO REMEMBER IN USING HUMOR
- Make it fit the story
- Have a reason
- Is not offensive
- Make it fit the audience
- Make it personal
- Make it count

PRACTICE, PRACTICE AND PRACTICE.

There are many people who have a natural ability to tell funny stories. Many consider it a talent. However, they probably have been telling stories and jokes for years. They didn't decide to be a funny speaker and then perfectly tell every story. It takes work. I know I have to work, rehearse, rehearse, practice, and practice. If you have ever taken a music lesson, did you become an overnight success after one lesson? Did you have to practice, practice and take many more lessons? And practice, practice and practice.

The negative people will laugh at you. You can't stop them. Positive people will encourage you all the way. Then the further up the ladder of success you travel you can laugh with yourself. Use humor where it is needed and you'll laugh all the way to the bank. You'll laugh to the head of the class. You'll laugh to excellent health!

When I was a teenager I was constantly being laughed at. I reached my height 5'8" by age 13 but only weighted 92 lbs. I was called, "beanpole, slats, Eiffel, Olive Oil." I wore braces so was called, "Dracula, Fang Woman, Tinsel mouth, Railroad Track." A group of boys, in my neighborhood sang a song about me that went like this: "Carol Dean with legs like toothpicks and a neck like a giraffe. Carol Dean got in the bathtub. Carol Dean pulled out the plug. Oh, my goodness! Oh my soul! There goes Carol Dean down that hole!"

I would run home crying to my momma. My mother, in her wisdom, said, "Carol Dean you are Somebody! Take the word *Somebody* and write it across your forehead.

Take the "S" and let it stand for Special because you are special.
Let the "O" stand for one, for there is only one of you.
The "M" - your mental attitude is great, if and when, you allow it to be.
The "E" is for enthusiasm. Live your life with enthusiasm, don't just walk through it.
"B" is beautiful; you are beautiful inside and out.
"O" others. Live your life for others for life is nothing without others.

"D" is deserving. You deserve the Best! That is why God created YOU.

And "Y" is for You. You are somebody, deserving, beautiful, Somebody Special.

So the next time, and any time, someone says something tacky to you. Put your shoulders back, hold your head up high, look them in the eye and ask, "Who on earth are you talking to? It can't be me, because I am Somebody Special!"
☺

Section II

Jokes

These jokes have been divided into different categories to help you in finding the right joke for your speech. However many jokes can be used in different categories. So use them as you see fit.

Also many, many of these jokes have come to me via e-mail and I have no idea who the originator was or is. So as we all know jokes are universal unless they are personal stories then they too can become universal. When you say something, it's out of your mouth into someone's ears and then on to the world.

Blonde
Church Jokes
Kids' Jokes
Men
Redneck
Tombstone or dead jokes
Tech jokes
Women
Jokes in General

BLONDE JOKES

1.) What do you call an eternity?
Four Blondes in four cars at a four way stop.
2.) Why do Blondes have TGIF written on their shoes?
Toes Go In First.
3.) Three Blondes were driving to Disneyland. After being in the car for four hours they finally saw a sign that said "Disneyland Left" so they turned around and went home.
4.) What do SMART Blondes and UFO's have in common?
You always hear about them but never see them.
5.) What did the Blonde say when she opened the box of Cheerios?
Oh look, Daddy...Doughnut seeds.
6.) Why did the Blonde stare at the can of frozen orange juice?
Because it said concentrate.
7.) Why do blondes always smile during lightning storms?
They think their picture is being taken.
8.) How can you tell when a Blonde sends you a fax?
It has a stamp on it.
9.) Why can't Blondes dial 911?
They can't find the 11 on the phone!
10.) What do you do if a Blonde throws a pin at you?
Run, she's got a grenade in her mouth!
11.) How can you tell if a Blonde has been using your computer?
There is whiteout all over the monitor.
12.) Why shouldn't Blondes have coffee breaks?
It takes too long to re-train them
13.) A Blonde and a brunette were walking outside when the brunette said, "Oh look at the dead bird." The Blonde looked skyward and said, "Where, where?"
14.) A brunette is standing on some train tracks, jumping from rail to rail, saying "21" "21" "21". A Blonde walks up, sees her and decides to join her. She also starts jumping from rail to rail saying "21" "21" "21". A Blonde walks up, sees her and decides to

join her.

She also starts jumping from rail to rail, saying "21" "21" "21". Suddenly, the brunette hears a train whistle and jumps off the tracks just as the Blonde is splattered all over the place. The Brunette goes back to jumping from rail to rail, counting "22" "22" "22".

15.) How do you drown a Blonde? Put a scratch & sniff sticker at the bottom of the pool.

16.) Why does it take longer to build a Blonde snowman as opposed to a regular one? You have to hollow out the head.

17.) How do you get a twinkle in a Blonde's eye? Shine a flashlight in her ear.

18.) Did you hear about the two Blondes that were found frozen to death in their car at the drive-in movie theater? They went to see "Closed for Winter"

19.) Two blondes were in a parking lot trying to unlock the door of their Mercedes with a coat hanger, but they couldn't. The girl with the coat hanger stopped for a moment to catch her breath and her friend said anxiously, "Hurry Up! It's starting to rain and the top is down!"

20.) What did the blonde say when she saw the sign in front of the YMCA? "Look! They spelled MACY'S wrong!"

21.) Why did the blonde scale the chain-link fence? To see what was on the other side.

22.) How do you make a blonde laugh on Saturday? Tell her a joke on Wednesday.

***

SHE'S JUST A BLONDE:

She put lipstick on her forehead because someone told her to make up her mind.

She got stabbed in a shoot out.

She told me to meet her at the corner of "walk" and don't walk.

She tried to put M&M's in alphabetical order.

She sat on the TV and watched the couch.

She tried to drown a fish.

She thought a quarterback was a refund.

She got locked in a grocery store and starved to death.

If you gave her a penny for intelligence, you'd get change back.

They had to burn the school down to get her out of third grade.

Under "education" on her job application, she put "hooked on phonics".

She tripped over a cordless phone.

She took a ruler to bed to see how long she slept.

At the bottom of the application where it says "sign here". . . She put "Sagittarius".

She asked for a price check at the dollar store.

It takes her two hours to watch 60 minutes.

If she spoke her mind, she'd probably be speechless.

She studied for a blood test, and failed.

She thought Boyz II Men was a daycare center.

She thought she needed a token to get on Soul Train.

She sold the car for gas money.

When she was the "NC-17 (under 17 not admitted), she went home and got 16 friends.

When she heard that 90% of all crimes occur around the home, she moved.

She thinks Taco Bell is where you pay your phone bill.

When she missed the 44 bus, she took the 22 bus twice instead.

When she went to the airport and saw a sign that said "airport left", she turned around and went home.

A young blonde was on vacation in the depths of Louisiana. She wanted a pair of genuine alligator shoes in the worst way, but was very reluctant to pay the high prices the local vendors were asking too much After becoming very frustrated with the "no haggle" attitude of one of the shopkeepers, the blonde shouted, "Maybe I'll just go out and catch my own alligator so I can get a pair of shoes at a reasonable price." The shopkeeper said, "Be all means, be my guest!"

Determined the blond headed for the swamps set on getting herself a big gator. Later the salesman was driving home spots the young woman standing waist deep in the water, shotgun in hand. Just then, he sees a huge 9 foot alligator swimming quickly towards her. She takes aim, kills the creature and with a great deal of effort hauls it on to the swamp bank. Laying nearby were several more of the dead creatures. The shopkeeper watches in amazement. Just then the blonde flips the alligator on its back, and frustrated, shouts out, "Dang it, this one isn't wearing any shoes either!"

A blonde was down on her luck. In order to raise some money, she decided to kidnap a kid and hold him for ransom. She went to the playground, grabbed a kid, took him behind a tree, and told him, "I've kidnapped you." She then wrote a note saying, "I've kidnapped your kid. Tomorrow morning , put $10,000 in a paper bad and put it under the pecan tree next to the slide on the north side of the playground. Signed, A Blonde." The Blonde then pinned the note to the kid's shirt and sent him home to show it to his parents. The next morning the blonde checked, and sure enough, a paper bag was sitting beneath the pecan tree. The Blonde opened the bag and found the $10,000 with a note that said, "How could you do this to another Blonde?"

☺

Church Jokes

1. Biblical questions to keep our minds clear. How well do you know the Bible??

♥ Why was Moses the most wicked man? (He broke all 10 commandments at once.)

♥ What kind of lights did Noah have on the ark? (Flood lights)

♥ How does a lawyer resemble a rabbi? (Lawyers study the law and the profits)

♥ What are the 2 smallest insects in the Bible? (The widow's mite (Mark 12:42) and the wicked flea (Proverbs 28:1))

♥ Who was the most ambitious man in the Bible? (Jonah-even a whale couldn't keep him down)

♥ Who was the first canning factory run by? (Noah-he had a boat full of preserved pairs)

♥ Why was Noah like a hungry cat? (He went 150 days without finding Ararat)

♥ What is it that Adam never saw or had, yet left 2 of them for his children? (Parents)

♥ What Bible character may have only been a foot tall? (Nicodemus-he was a ruler)

♥ What did Jesus have in common with the fish that swallowed Jonah? (Jesus had dinner with a sinner, and the fish had a sinner for dinner)

♥ How do we know Isaiah's parents were good business people? (They both raised a prophet)

♥ During what season did Eve eat the forbidden fruit? (Early in the fall)

♥ Why couldn't they play cards on the ark? (Noah was sitting on the deck)

♥ Why did poor Job land in bed with a cold? (He had poor comforters)

♥ How are rollerbladers like the fruit in the Garden of Eden? (They come before the fall)

♥ Who introduced salted meat to the Navy? (Noah-he took Ham on the ark)

♥ Who slept five in a bed? (David-he slept with his forefathers)

- Why did the people on the ark think the horses were pessimistic? (They kept saying neigh)
- How do we know Abraham was smart?   (He knew a Lot)
- What was one of the first example of math in the Bible? (God told Adam to go forth and multiply)
- Why couldn't Cain please God with his offering?   (He just wasn't Abel)
- How did God keep the oceans clean?   (With Tide)
- What did Noah say as he was loading the Ark?   ("Now I herd everything")
- What was the name of Isaiah's horse?   (Isme" - He said "Whoa, is-me!")
- Was Noah the first one out of the Ark?   (No, he came forth out of the ark)

2. The minister was preoccupied with thoughts of how he was going to ask the congregation to come up with more money than they were expecting for repairs to the church building.

Therefore, he was annoyed to find that the regular organist was sick and a substitute had been brought in at the last minute. The substitute wanted to know what to play.

"Here's a copy of the service," he said impatiently. "But you'll have to think of something to play after I make the announcement about the finances."

During the service, the minister paused and said, "Brothers and Sisters, we are in great difficulty; the roof repairs cost twice as much as we expected, and we need $4,000 more. Any of you who can pledge $100 or more, please stand up."

At that moment, the substitute organist played "The Star-Spangled Banner."

And that is how the substitute organist became the permanent organist!

3.   A friend was in front of me coming out of church one day, and the preacher was standing at the door as he always was to shake hands. He grabbed my friend by the hand and pulled him aside. The Pastor said to him, "You need to join the Army of the Lord!"

My friend replied, "I'm already in the Army of the Lord, Pastor." Pastor questioned, "How come I don't see you except at Christmas and Easter?" He whispered back, "I'm in the secret service."

4. A young boy had just gotten his driving permit. He asked his father, who was a minister, if they could discuss the use of the car. His father took him to his study and said to him, "I'll make a deal with you. You bring your grades up, study your Bible a little and get your hair cut and we'll talk about it."

After about a month the boy came back and again asked his father if they could discuss use of the car. They again went to the father's study where his father said, "Son, I've been real proud of you. You have brought your grades up, you've studied your Bible diligently, but you didn't get your hair cut!"

The young man waited a moment and replied, "You know Dad, I've been thinking about that. You know, Samson had long hair, Moses had long hair, Noah had long hair, and even Jesus had long hair."

To which his father replied, "Yes, and they walked every where they went!"

5. For Show-N-Tell, a teacher asked her pupils to bring something which would symbolize their religion. One little boy brought a Star of David and said "I am Jewish and this is the symbol of our religion." A little girl brought a crucifix and said, "I am Catholic and this is the symbol of our religion." Another little boy held up a casserole and said "I'm a Methodist."

6. Two deacons were trying to impress each other with how spiritual they were. One of them in exasperation said, "Why, I'll bet $10 you can't even say the Lord's prayer!" The other responded, "I'll take you up on that bet." So he began, "Now I lay me down to sleep, I pray the Lord my soul to keep. If I should die before I wake, I pray the Lord my soul to take." There was a moment of silence and then the other deacon said, "Well, here's your money. I never thought you could do it."

7. The preacher bought a new pickup so he and his wife loaded some of the deacons in the back end to take them for a ride. The preacher accidentally lost control of the pickup which plunged into the lake. In a moment, the preacher and his wife surfaced and swam to shore. They looked for the deacons, but none appeared. They waited and waited until they began to really worry when suddenly one of the deacons surfaced, then another and another until all were accounted for. The preacher said, "What took you so long. We were really getting worried about you." One of the deacons replied, "You know these new vehicles. It took us a good while to figure out how to open the tailgate!"

8. A man who smelled like a distillery flopped on a subway seat next to a priest. The man's tie was stained, his face was plastered with red lipstick, and a half empty bottle of gin was sticking out of his torn coat pocket. He opened his newspaper and began reading. After a few minutes the disheveled guy turned to the priest and asked, "Say, Father, what causes arthritis?"

"Mister, it's caused by loose living, being with cheap, wicked women, too much alcohol, and a contempt for your fellow man."

"Well, I'll be darned," the drunk muttered, returning to his paper. The priest, thinking about what he had said, nudged the man and apologized. "I'm very sorry, I didn't mean to come on so strong. How long have you had arthritis?"

"I don't have it, Father. I was just reading here that the Pope does."

9. TOP TEN REASONS GOD CREATED EVE

10. God worried that Adam would always be lost in the garden because men hate to ask for directions.

9. God knew that Adam would one day need someone to hand him the TV remote. (Men don't want to see what's on television, they want to see WHAT ELSE is on!)

8. God knew that Adam would never buy a new fig leaf when his wore out and would therefore need Eve to get one for him.

7. God knew that Adam would never make a doctor's appointment for himself.

6. God knew that Adam would never remember which night was

garbage night.

5. God knew that if the world was to be populated, men would never be able to handle childbearing.

4. As "Keeper of the Garden," Adam would never remember where he put his tools.

3. The scripture account of creation indicates Adam needed someone to blame his troubles on when God caught him hiding in the garden.

2. As the Bible says, "It is not good for man to be alone!" (That's when he usually gets into trouble)

1. When God finished the creation of Adam, He stepped back, scratched His head and said, "I can do better than that!"

10. A pastor saw a group of about a dozen boys, all between 10 and 12, surrounding a dog. Concerned, the pastor asked, "What are you boys doing with that old dog?" One of the boys replied, "This dog is just an old neighborhood stray. We all want him. So we've decided whoever can tell the biggest lie gets him."

The pastor, hoping to teach a lesson, said, "Don't you boys know it's a sin to lie? Why, when I was your age, I never told a lie." There was dead silence. Then the youngest boy said with a deep sigh, "All right. Give him the dog."

11. Senility Prayer
God, grant me the Senility
To forget the people
I never liked anyway,
The good fortune
To run into the ones I do,
And the eyesight
To tell the difference.

12. In Sunday School one morning little six year-old Brett was asked to recite his favorite bible verse. He replied, "You cannot live by bread alone. You got to have peanut butter."

13. The old farmer thought everyone was against him. While out

in the field praying one day a bird flew over and 'Splat' right on the man's face. The farmer said, "See Lord; for some the birds sing!"

14. Leaving church one morning the mother was constantly complaining. The music was too loud, the pews too hard, the sermon too long. Her daughter said, "Well Ma, what did you expect for a dollar?"

15. A woman went to heaven but kept standing outside the golden gates while others went right on in. Finally, Saint Peter approached her and said, 'Lady, it's okay. You can go inside." She sobbingly replied, "I can't. I didn't bring a covered dish!"

16. A Sunday School teacher was asking the children if they knew where God lives. One little boy stated that he knew for sure that God lives in their bathroom. The teacher asked him why. He stated, "Ever morning my daddy pounds on the bathroom door. He then exclaims, "My God, are you still in there?"

17. After a young minister preached his first sermon, one parishioner whispered to another, "If he heard the 'call for the ministry', he must have been eavesdropping."

18. A young boy asked the minister what Jesus' first words were when he left the tomb. The minister asked, "You mean when he spoke to the angel?" The young boy, said, "No, I mean his first words when he stepped from the tomb." The minister stated that he wasn't sure. The boy replied, "Ta Da!"

19. One little girl was asked if she knew the 10 commandments. "Well," she sated, I think one is to laugh a lot because it is to Humor thy father and mother."

20. The bell choir couldn't decide on their name. Should they be called, "The Holy Tollers" or "The Ding-a-lings?"

21. The choir director's son told his father that he couldn't wait to hear the choir sing, "Lead On Oh Kinky Turtle." (Lead On Oh, King Eternal)

22. Little Jimmy was asked what song he liked the most in Sunday School. He answered, "Gladly the Cross Eyed Bear." (Gladly the Cross I'd Bear.)

23. Two young boys were arguing what God's first name was. One of them said, "It is Howard, You have heard them said, 'Howard be thy name." The other boy said, "No, No, it is Andy. You have heard 'Andy walks with me."

24. Funny Sayings from Church Bulletins:
1. Scouts are saving aluminum cans, bottles, and other items to be recycled. Proceeds will be used to cripple children.
2. Ushers will eat latecomers.
3. The Ladies Bible Study will be held Thursday morning at 10am. All ladies are invited to lunch in the Fellowship Hall after the BS is done.
4. The Pastor would appreciate it if the ladies of the congregation would lend him their electric girdles for the pancake breakfast next Sunday morning.
5. The audience is asked to remain seated until the end of the recession.
6. Low Self-Esteem Support Group will meet Thursday at 7 to 8:30 PM. Please use the back door.
7. Pastor is on vacation. Massages can be given to church secretary.
8. The third verse of Blessed Assurance will be sung without musical accomplishment.
9. The Rev. Merriwether spoke briefly, much to the delight of the audience.
10. The pastor will preach his farewell message, after which the choir will sing, 'Break Forth Into Joy.'
11. Next Sunday Mrs. Vinson will be soloist for the morning service. The pastor will then speak on 'It's a Terrible Experience'.

12. Due to the Rector's illness, Wednesday's healing services will be discontinued until further notice.

13. Weight Watchers will meet at 7 PM. Please use large double door at the side entrance.

14. Remember in prayer the many who are sick of our church and community.

15. The eighth graders will be presenting Shakespeare's Hamlet in the church basement on Friday at 7 PM. The congregation is invited to attend this tragedy.

16. A song fest was hell at the Methodist church Wednesday.

17. Today's Sermon: 'How Much Can a Man Drink?' with hymns from a full choir.

18. On a church bulletin during the minister's illness: God is good. Dr. Hargreaves is better.

19. Potluck supper: prayer and medication to follow.

20. The outreach committee has enlisted 25 visitors to make calls on people who are not afflicted with any church.

21. Eight new choir robes are currently needed, due to the addition of several new members and the deterioration of some older ones.

22. The choir invites any member of the congregation who enjoys sinning to join the choir.

25. A country preacher decided to skip services one Sunday and head to the hills to do some bear hunting. As he rounded the corner on a perilous twist in the trail, he and a bear collided, sending him and his rifle tumbling down the mountainside. Before he knew it, his rifle went one way and he went the other, landing on a rock and breaking both legs. That was the good news. The bad news was the ferocious bear charging at him from a distance, and he couldn't move. "Oh Lord," the preacher prayed, "I'm so sorry for skipping services today to come out here and hunt. Please forgive me and grant me just one wish....please make a Christian out of that bear that's coming at me. Please, Lord!" That very instant, the bear skidded to a halt, fell to its knees, clasped its paws together and began to pray aloud right at the preacher's feet. "Dear God, bless

this food I am about to receive."

26. A Christian couple wanted to get a family pet. They felt it important to own a Christian trained pet. So, they went pet searching. At a kennel specializing in Christian trained pets, they found a dog they liked quite a lot. When they asked the dog to fetch the Bible, he did it in a flash. When they instructed him to look up Psalm 23, he complied equally fast using his paws with dexterity. They were impressed, purchased the animal, and went home.

That night they had friends over. They were so proud of their new dog and his major skills, they called the dog over and had him show off his Bible fetching ability. The friends ask whether the dog was able to do any of the usual dog tricks, as well. This stopped the couple cold, as they hadn't thought about 'normal' tricks. They said, "Let's try it out."

Once more they called the dog, and clearly pronounced the command, "Heel!" Immediately the dog jumped up, put his paw on the man's forehead closed his eyes in concentration, and bowed his head.

27. Bible in 50 words
God made - Adam bit -- Noah arked -- Abraham split -- Joseph ruled - Jacob fooled — Bush talked —   Moses balked -- Pharaoh plagued -- People walked —Sea divided -- Tablets guided - Promise landed -- Saul freaked — David peeked --   Prophets warned -- Jesus born -- God walked — Love talked — Anger crucified -- Hope died -- Love rose — Spirit flamed -- Word spread -- God remained.

28. One Sunday a pastor told his congregation that the church needed some extra money and asked the people to prayerfully consider giving a little extra in the offering plate. He said that whoever gave the most would be able to pick out three hymns. After the offering plates were passed, the pastor glanced down and noticed that someone had placed a $1,000 bill in offering. He was so excited that he immediately shared his joy with his congregation and

said he'd like to personally thank the person who placed the money in the plate. A very quiet, elderly, saintly lady all the way in the back shyly raised her hand. The pastor asked her to come to the front. He told her how wonderful it was that she gave so much and in thanksgiving asked her to pick out three hymns. Her eyes brightened as she looked over the congregation, pointed to the three handsomest men in the building and said, "I'll take him, him & him."

29. One Sunday there were so many songs sung that the preacher decided the next week there just wouldn't be any music. The choir director argued that music is too important to be left out. He stated, "Just give me one more chance and let's see what happens. The next Sunday morning the choir director told the congregation how important music is and asked if they didn't have certain songs associated with certain words. "In fact," he said, "If you think of a song when I say a word, just start singing it." He then said, 'water' and a gentleman on the left side on the church began singing "Shall We Gather At The River." They sang all four versus. Then the choir director said, "Bird." A woman on the right side of the church began singing, "And His Eye Is On The Sparrow." They sang all four versus. Then the choir director said, "Sex." There was total quietness across the congregation until the white-haired woman on the back row began singing, "Precious Memories."

30. You know why Jesus was born in a manger don't you? His parents had HMO and the innkeeper was not an approved provider.

31. Two young brothers were always getting into mischief. It didn't seem what the parents did to punish them the mischief continued. The parents decided they would have the pastor talk to the boys. The pastor took the younger boy in his office and asked, "Where is God?" The little boy said nothing. So the pastor repeated, "Where is God?" Sill the young boy said nothing. Finally the pastor almost shouted, "Do you know where God is?" With that the little boy jumped up and ran out of the room. He grabbed his brother and said, "Let's get out of here. God is missing and they think we had something to do with it?" ☺

Kids Jokes

1. A little boy was in a relative's wedding. As he was coming down the aisle he would take two steps, stop, and turn to the crowd (alternating between bride's side and groom's side). While facing the crowd, he would put his hands up like claws and ROAR. So it went, step by step, ROAR, step by step, ROAR all the way down the aisle. As you can imagine, by the time he reached the pulpit, the crowd was near tears from laughing so hard. The little boy, however, was getting more and more distressed from all the laughing, and was also near tears by the time he reached the pulpit. When asked what he was doing, the child sniffed and said, "I was being the Ring Bear..."

2. The boss of a big company needed to call one of his employees about an urgent problem with one of the main computers. He dialed the employees home phone number and was greeted with a child's whisper on the first ring, "Hello?" Feeling put out at the inconvenience of having to talk to a youngster the boss asked, "Is your Daddy home?" "Yes," whispered the small voice. May I talk with him?" the man asked. To the surprise of the boss, the small voice whispered, "No." Wanting to talk with an adult, the boss asked, "Is your Mommy there?" "Yes," came the answer. "May I talk with her?" Again the small voice whispered, "No." Knowing it was not likely a young child would be left home alone, the boss decided he would just leave a message with the person who should be there watching over the child. "Is there any one there besides you?" the boss asked the child. "Yes," whispered the child, "A policeman." Wondering what a cop would be doing at his employee's home, the boss asked, "May I speak with the policeman?" "No, he's busy," whispered the child. "Busy doing what?" asked the boss. "Talking to Daddy and Mommy and the Fireman," came the whispered answer. Growing concerned and even worried as he heard what sounded like a helicopter through the ear piece on the phone the boss asked, "What is that noise?" "A hello-copper," answered the whispering voice. "What is going on there?" asked the boss, now alarmed. In an awed whispering voice the child answered,

"The search team just landed the hello-copper!" Alarmed, concerned and more than just a little frustrated the boss asked, "Why are they there?" Still whispering, the young voice replied along with a muffled giggle, "They're looking for me!"

3. A three-year-old boy went with his dad to see a litter of kittens. On returning home, he breathlessly informed his mother, "There were 2 boy kittens and 2 girl kittens." "How did you know?" his mother asked. "Daddy picked them up and looked underneath," he replied. "I think it's printed on the bottom."

4. A three-year-old boy put his shoes on by himself. His mother noticed the left was on the right foot. She said, "Son, your shoes are on the wrong feet." He looked up at her with a raised brow and said, "Don't kid me, Mom. I KNOW they're my feet."

5. On the first day of school, the Kindergarten teacher said, "If anyone has to go to the bathroom, hold up two fingers. A little voice from the back of the room asked, "How will that help?"

6. A mother and her young son returned from the grocery store and began putting away the groceries. The boy opened the box of animal crackers and spread them all over the table. "What are you doing?" his mother asked. "The box says you can't eat them if the seal is broken," the boy explained. "I'm looking for the seal."

7. "Can people predict the future with cards?" "My mother can." "Really?" "Yes, she takes one look at my report card and tells me what will happen when my father gets home."

8. A father was reading Bible stories to his young son. He read, "The man named Lot was warned to take his wife and flee out of the city, but his wife looked back and was turned to salt." His son asked, "What happened to the flea?"

9. A four-year-old girl was learning to say the Lord's Prayer. She was reciting it all by herself without help from her mother. She

said, "And lead us not into temptation, but deliver us some e-mail. AMEN."

10. Robert, age eight, was the son of strict Presbyterian parents. He was very, very good, worked hard at school, did his chores, and was generally helpful and obedient. But one morning, for some reason, he came down to breakfast in a very nasty mood. When his mother served him prunes, he snarled, "I don't want prunes," and he refused to eat them. His parents were aghast, and his father said, "Robert, you know God commanded children to honor and obey their parents, and He will punish those who do not."
But Robert still refused and was angrily sent back to bed, and the prunes were put in the refrigerator.
A few minutes later, a terrible thunderstorm came up with great roars and flashes of lightning. "Ah, wonderful," said Robert's mother, "this will teach him a lesson." Robert came back down the stairs, went into the kitchen and opened the fridge. From there, just after another flash and roar, the boy's voice was heard saying, "Heck of a fuss to make about a few stupid prunes."

11. Kids Perspectives - The U.S. Flag: The kindergarten teacher was showing her class an encyclopedia page picturing several national flags. She pointed to the American flag and asked, "What flag is this?" A little girl called out, "That's the flag of our country." "Very good," the teacher said. "And what is the name of our country?" 'Tis of thee," the girl said confidently.

12. FUNNY THINGS FROM KIDS
After putting her children to bed, a mother changed into old slacks and a droopy blouse and proceeded to wash her hair. As she heard the children getting more and more rambunctious, her patience grew thin. At last she threw a towel around her head and stormed into their room, putting them back to bed with stern warnings. As she left the room, she heard her three-year-old say with a trembling voice, "Who was that?"

13. Two little boys were visiting their grandfather and he took

them to a restaurant for lunch. They couldn't make up their minds about what they wanted to eat. Finally the grandfather grinned at the server and said, "Just bring them bread and water." One of the little boys looked up and with a quavering voice, "Can I have ketchup on it?"

14. A new neighbor asked the little girl next door if she had any brothers and sisters. She replied, "No, I'm the lonely child."

15. A mother was telling her little girl what her own childhood was like: "We used to skate outside on a pond. I had a swing made from a tire; it hung from a tree in our front yard. We rode our pony. We picked wild raspberries in the woods." The little girl was wide-eyed, taking this in. At last she said, "I sure wish I'd gotten to know you sooner!"

16. A little girl was diligently pounding away on her father's word processor. She told him she was writing a story. "What's it about?" he asked. "I don't know," she replied. "I can't read."

17. I didn't know if my granddaughter had learned her colors yet, so I decided to test her. I would point out something and ask what color it was. She would tell me, and always she was correct. But it was fun for me, so I continued. At last she headed for the door, saying sagely, "Grandma, I think you should try to figure out some of these yourself!"

18. A ten-year-old, under the tutelage of her grandmother, was becoming quite knowledgeable about the Bible. Then one day she floored her grandmother by asking, "Which Virgin was the mother of Jesus: the virgin Mary or the King James Virgin?"

19. A Sunday School class was studying the Ten Commandments. They were ready to discuss the last one. The teacher asked if anyone could tell her what it was. Susie raised her hand, stood tall, and quoted, "Thou shall not take the covers off thy neighbor's wife."

20. A six-year-old comes crying to his Mother because his little sister pulled his hair. "Don't be angry," the Mother says, "Your little sister doesn't realize pulling hair hurts."
A short while later, there's more crying, and the Mother goes to investigate. This time the sister is bawling and her brother says... "Now she knows."

21. A little boy was looking through the family album and asked his mother: "Who's this guy on the beach with you with all the muscles and curly hair?" "That's your father," his mom replied. "Well," he asked, "then who's the old bald-headed man who lives with us now?"

22. A little boy opened the big and old family Bible with fascination, and looked at the old pages as he turned them. Suddenly, something fell out of the Bible, and he picked it up and looked at it closely. It was an old leaf from a tree that had been pressed in between the pages.
"Momma, look what I found," the boy called out. "What have you got there, dear?" his mother asked. With astonishment in the young boy's voice, he answered: "I think it's Adam's suit!"

23. A third grade teacher was using yellow as an example in explaining how to divide words in syllables. A little boy raised his hand and exclaimed the word reminded him of teachers. "Why?" "Because they yell at you when you make a low grade."

24. Two young boys were talking about how smart their grandmother was. One of them said, "Yeah, but she not too smart on everything. I looked at her driver's license. She got an 'F' in sex."

25. You know why Six is afraid of Seven? Because seven eight nine!

26. Why did the chicken cross the school yard? To get to the other slide.

27. When a student asked how to get the skin off the frog in biology one teacher stated, "Ripit! Ripit! Ripit!"

28. Smiling is infectious, you catch it like the flu.
When someone smiled at me today, I started smiling too.
I passed around the corner, and someone saw my grin
When he smiled I realized, I'd passed it on to him.

I thought about that smile, then I realized its worth,
A single smile, just like mine, could travel round the earth.
So, if you feel a smile begin, don't leave it undetected
Let's start an epidemic quick and get the world infected!

29. One Father's Day, a grandpa was spending the day with his grandchildren. His granddaughter wanted to go play with the little neighbor girl. Her mother told her she couldn't go anywhere while she had company. Several hours later the girl climbed on her grandpa's lap, and asked, "Grandpa, isn't it time you went home?"

30. Two little boys spent the night with their neighbor and had even eaten supper with them. The next morning the lady of the house was doing other things and had not started breakfast yet. About 30 minutes after the boys got up the older one said, "You know, Peggy, at our house we eat in the mornings too!"

31. One little boy kept telling his mother how scared he was during a thunder storm and asked her to sleep with him. She said, "Now Joey, you know there is no reason to be afraid. Jesus is right here with you." Joey said, "Yeah, I know it but right now I would like to feel some skin."

32. My granddaughter was telling her class what her parents and grandparents do for a living. When she got to her speaker grandmother (me) she said, "She gets all dressed up, goes to hotels, makes lots of money and comes home really tired."

33. A mother was preparing pancakes for her sons, Kevin, 5, Ryan, 3. The boys began to argue over who would get the first pancake. Their mother saw the opportunity for a moral lesson. "If Jesus were sitting here, He would say, 'Let my brother have the first pancake. I can wait.' Kevin turned to his younger brother and said, "Ryan, you be Jesus!"

34. Quotes from science exam by 11 year-old students:
"When you breathe, you inspire. When you don't, you expire.
"H_2O is hot water, CO_2 is cold water."
"When you smell an odorless gas, it is probably carbon monoxide"
"Three kinds of blood vessels are arteries, vanes and caterpillars."
"The moon is a planet just like the earth, only it is deader."
"Rhubarb: a kind of celery gone bloodshot."
"Vacuum: a large empty space where the Pope lives."
"To keep milk from turning sour, keep it in the cow."
"The skeleton is what is left after the insides have been taken out and the outsides have been taken off. The purpose of the skeleton is something to hitch meat to."
"Magnet: something you find crawling all over a dead cat."
"Germinate: to become a naturalized German."

35. A Scoutmaster was teaching his Boy Scouts about survival in the desert. "What are the three most important things you should bring with you in case you get lost in the desert?" he asked.
Several hands went up, and many important things were suggested such as food, matches, etc. The Scoutmaster wanted to make sure all scouts participated so he kept asking for suggestions.
Then one little boy in the back eagerly raised his hand. "Yes, Timmy, what are the three most important things you'd bring?" "A compass, a canteen of water, and a deck of cards." "I understand the need for a compass so you can find your direction, and I agree a canteen of water is necessary, but why do you think you'll need a deck of cards?" "Well, sir, even if stranded in the desert, as soon as you start playing Solitaire, someone is bound to come up behind you and say, 'Put that red nine on top of the black ten!"

36. WHAT KIDS HAVE LEARNED:

1. If you hook a dog leash over a ceiling fan, the motor is not strong enough to rotate a 42 pound boy wearing puppy underwear and a superman cape.

2. A ceiling fan motor is strong enough, however, to spread paint on all four walls of a 20 by 20 foot room.

3. When you hear the toilet flush and the words "Uh-oh," it's already too late.

4. Brake fluid mixed with Clorox makes smoke, and lots of it.

5. A six year old can start a fire with a flint rock even though a 36 year old man says they can only do it in the movies.

6. If you use a waterbed as home plate while wearing baseball shoes it does not leak - it explodes.

7. A king size waterbed holds enough water to fill a 2000 sq. foot house 4 inches deep.

8. LEGOS will pass through the digestive tract of a four year old.

9. Super glue is forever.

10. McGyver can teach us many things we don't want to know.

11. No matter how much Jell-O you put in a swimming pool you still can't walk on water.

12. Pool filters do not like Jell-O.

13. VCR's do not eject PB&J sandwiches even though TV commercials show they do.

14. Always look in the oven before you turn it on.

15. The fire department in San Jose has at least a 5 minute response time.

16. The spin cycle on the washing machine does not make earth worms dizzy.

17. It will however make cats dizzy.

18. Cats throw up twice their body weight when dizzy.

37. PAID IN FULL

A little boy came up to his mother in the kitchen one evening while she was fixing supper, and he handed her a piece of paper that he had been writing on. After his mom dried her hands on an apron, she read it, and this is what it said:

For cutting the grass: $5.00

For cleaning up my room this week: $1.00
For going to the store for you: .50
Baby-sitting my kid brother while you went shopping: .25
Taking out the garbage: $1.00
For getting a good report card: $5.00
For cleaning up and raking the yard: $2.00

Total owed: $14.75

Well, his mother looked at him standing there, and the boy could see the memories flashing through her mind. She picked up the pen, turned over the paper he'd written on, and this is what she wrote:

For the nine months I carried you while you were growing inside me: No Charge.

For all the nights that I've sat up with you, doctored and prayed for you: No Charge.

For all the trying times, and all the tears that you've caused through the years: No Charge.

For all the nights that were filled with dread, and for the worries I knew were ahead: No Charge.

For the toys, food, clothes, and even wiping your nose:
No Charge, Son.

When you add it up, the cost of my love is: No Charge.

When the boy finished reading what his mother had written, there were big tears in his eyes, and he looked straight up at his mother and said, "Mom, I sure do love you." And then he took the pen and in great big letters he wrote: "PAID IN FULL".

38. Things my mother taught me...

My Mother taught me LOGIC - like, "If you fall off that swing and break your neck, you can't go to the store with me."

My Mother taught me MEDICINE - like, "If you don't stop cross-ing your eyes, they're going to freeze that way."

My Mother taught me ESP - "Put your sweater on; don't you think I know when you are cold?"

My Mother taught me TO MEET A CHALLENGE - "Where's your

brother and don't talk with food in your mouth. Answer me!"
My Mother taught me HUMOR - "When that lawnmower cuts off
your toes, don't come running to me."

39.   A young mother and her four-year old daughter were going
down the highway when they were stopped by a patrolman. The
patrolman asked the woman if she knew why she was being
stopped. The woman responded, "I guess I was speeding." The
officer said, "Yes madam, you were going 65 in s 45 mile hour
zone." At that point the little girl shouted, "Sixty five! What were
you trying to do, kill me?" The officer smiled, then she added,
"And you know what? I have had my seat belt on since I got in the
car, and she just put her's on when you started walking up." The
officer smiled more and just issued a warning ticket. He seemed to
think the woman has enough to keep her occupied.

40.   Blair, one of my granddaughters, and I were visiting a friend
of mine who is a little older than I am. Blair needed to brush her
hair but we didn't have a brush with us. She asked me, "Cha Cha,
do you think that girl, (my older friend) would have a brush?"
Needless to say, My friend Bonnie was elated to be called a 'girl.'
Maybe Blair should go in to politics.
☺

Men's Jokes

1. Reasons To Be A Guy

Phone conversations are over in 30 seconds flat.

You know stuff about tanks.

Dry cleaners and hair cutters don't rob you blind.

You can quietly enjoy a car ride from a passenger's seat.

Wedding dress - $2,000; Tuxedo rental $75.

You don't mooch off others' desserts.

You spend only half as much for earrings.

A 5-day trip requires only one suitcase.

We can open all our own jars.

We can go to the bathroom without a support group.

We don't have to learn how to spell a new last name.

We can leave a motel bed unmade.

We can kill our own food.

We get extra credit for the slightest act of thoughtfulness.

Wedding plans take care of themselves.

If someone forgets to invite us to something, they can still be our friend.

Underwear is $10 a three-pack.

If you are 34 and single, nobody notices.

Everything on our faces stays in the original color.

Three pair of shoes are more than enough.

We don't have to clean the apartment if the meter reader is coming.

Car mechanics tell us the truth.

We can sit quietly and watch a game with a friend for hours without thinking "He must be mad at me."

Same work - more pay.

Gray hair and wrinkles only add character.

We can drop by and see a friend without having to bring a little gift.

If another guy shows up at a party in the same outfit, you just might become life long friends.

Your pals will never trap you with: "So, notice anything different?"

We are not expected to know the names of more than 5 colors.

We almost never have a "strap problem" in public.

We are totally unable to see wrinkles in our clothes.
The same hairstyle lasts for years - maybe decades.
We don't have to shave below the neck.
A few belches are expected and tolerated.
Our belly usually hides our big hips.
One wallet, one pair of shoes, one color, all seasons.
We can do our nails with a pocketknife.
We have freedom of choice concerning growing a mustache.
Christmas shopping can be accomplished for 25 people on the day before Christmas and in 45 minutes.

2. A man complained to his barber he couldn't get a close enough shave. The barber had a solution. He handed the man a small wooden ball, "Just place this between your cheek and gum while I give you a shave." The man did so and started receiving the closest shave he could remember. Toward the end of the shave, he asked, "What if I swallow the ball?" "No problem" the barber said, "If you do, just bring it back tomorrow like everyone else does."

3. Men and Women compared:
NICKNAMES: If Emma, Suzanne, Debra and Michelle go out for lunch, they will call each other Emma, Suzanne, Debra and Michelle. But if Mike, Phil, Rob and Jack go out for a pint, they will affectionately refer to each other as Fat Boy, Godzilla, Peanut-Head and Useless.

EATING OUT: When the bill arrives, Mike, Phil, Rob and Jack will each throw in $20, even though it's only for $22.50. None of them will have anything smaller, and none will actually admit they want change back. When the girls get their bill, out come the pocket calculators.

MONEY: A man will pay $2 for a $1 item he wants. A woman will pay $1 for a $2 item she doesn't want.

BATHROOMS: A man has six items in his bathroom-a toothbrush, shaving cream, razor, a bar of soap, and a towel from the Holiday Inn. The average number of items in the typical woman's bathroom is 437. A man would not be able to identify most of these items.

ARGUMENTS: A woman has the last word in any argument. Anything a man says after that is the beginning of a new argument.

CATS: Women love cats. Men say they love cats, but when women aren't looking, men kick cats.

FUTURE: A woman worries about the future until she gets a husband. A man never worries about the future until he gets a wife.

SUCCESS: A successful man is one who makes more money than his wife can spend. A successful woman is one who can find such a man.

MARRIAGE: A woman marries a man expecting he will change, but he doesn't. A man marries a woman expecting she won't change and she does.

DRESSING UP: A woman will dress up to: go shopping, water the plants, empty the garbage, answer the phone, read a book, get the mail. A man will dress up for: weddings, funerals.

NATURAL: Men wake up as good-looking as they went to bed. Women somehow deteriorate during the night.

OFFSPRING: Ah, children. A woman knows all about her children. She knows about dentist appointments and romances, best friends and favorite foods and secret fears and hopes and dreams. A man is vaguely aware of some short people living in the house.

4. A guy sticks his head in the barber shop and asks "How long before I can get a haircut?" The barber looks around the shop and says, "About 2 hours." The guy leaves. A few days later, the same guy sticks his head in the door and asks, "How long before I get a haircut?" The barber looks around the shop full of customers and

says, "About 2 hours."

The guy leaves. A week later, the same guy sticks his head in the shop and asks, "How long before I can get a haircut?"

The barber looks around the shop an says, "About an hour and half."

The guy leaves. The barber looks over at a friend in the shop, and says, "Hey Bill, follow that guy and see where he goes."

In a little while, Bill comes back into the shop laughing hysterically. The barber asks, "Bill, where did he go when he left here?" Bill looked up and said, "To your house."

5. A pastor, a doctor and an engineer were waiting one morning for a particularly slow group of golfers. The engineer fumed, "What's with these guys?" "We must have been waiting for 15 minutes!" The doctor chimed in, "I don't know, but I've never seen such ineptitude!" The pastor said, "Hey, here comes the greens keeper. Let's have a word with him."

"Hi George. Say, what's with that group ahead of us? They're rather slow, aren't they?" The greens keeper replied, "Oh, yes, that's a group of blind firefighters. They lost their sight saving our clubhouse from a fire last year, so we always let them play for free anytime." The group was silent for a moment. The pastor said, "That's so sad. I think I will say a special prayer for them tonight. "

The doctor said, "Good idea. And I'm going to contact my ophthalmologist buddy and see if there's anything he can do for them." The engineer said, "Why can't these guys play at night?"

6. Letter to Dad:

Dear Dad,

$chool i$ really great. I am making lot$ of friend$ and $tudying very hard. With all my $tuff, I $imply can't think of anything I need, $o if you would like, you can ju$t $end me a card, a$ I would love to hear from you.

Love,

Your $on

The Reply:

Dear Son,

I kNOw that astroNOmy, ecoNOmics, and oceaNOgraphy are

eNOugh to keep even an hoNOr student busy. Do NOt forget that the pursuit of kNOwledge is a NOble task, and you can never study eNOugh.

Love,
Dad

7. An Aggie, a sheep, and a dog were survivors of a terrible shipwreck. They found themselves stranded on a desert island. After being there a while, they got into the habit of going to the beach every evening to watch the sun go down. One particular evening, the sky was red with beautiful Cirrus clouds; the breeze was warm and gentle, a perfect night for romance. As they sat there, the sheep started looking better and better to the Aggie. Soon, he leaned over to the sheep and put his arm around it. But the dog got jealous, growling fiercely until the Aggie took his arm from around the sheep. After that, the three of them continued to enjoy the sunsets together, but there was no more cuddling.

A few weeks passed by, and low and behold, there was another shipwreck. The only survivor was a beautiful young woman, the most beautiful woman the Aggie had ever seen. She was in a pretty bad way when they rescued her and they slowly nursed her back to health. When the young maiden was well enough, they introduced her to their evening beach ritual. It was another beautiful evening: red sky, cirrus clouds, a warm and gentle breeze; perfect for a night of romance. Pretty soon, the Aggie started to get "those feelings" again. He fought them as long as he could, but he finally gave in and leaned over to the young woman, cautiously, and whispered in her ear..........."Would you mind taking the dog for a walk?"

8. PARENTAL EXCUSES
These are actual excuse notes from parents (including original spelling):
My son is under a doctor's care and should not take P.E. today. Please execute him.
Please excuse Lisa for being absent. She was sick and I had her shot.

Dear School: Please ekscuse John being absent on Jan. 28, 29, 30, 31, 32, and also 33.

Please excuse Roland from P.E. for a few days. Yesterday he fell out of a tree and misplaced his hip.

John has been absent because he had two teeth taken out of his face.

Carlos was absent yesterday because he was playing football. He was hurt in the growing part.

Megan could not come to school today because she has been bothered by very close veins.

Chris will not be in school cus he has an acre in his side.

Please excuse Ray Friday from school. He has very loose vowels.

Please excuse Tommy for being absent yesterday. He had diarrhea and his boots leak.

Irving was absent yesterday because he missed his bust.

Please excuse Jimmy for being. It was his father's fault.

I kept Billie home because she had to go Christmas shopping because I don't know what size she wear.

Please excuse Jennifer for missing school yesterday. We forgot to get the Sunday paper off the porch, and when we found it Monday, we thought it was Sunday.

Sally won't be in school a week from Friday. We have to attend her funeral.

Please excuse Jason for being absent yesterday. He had a cold and could not breed well.

Please excuse Burma, she has been sick and under the doctor.

9. Bob Hill and his new wife Betty were vacationing in Europe, as it happens, near Transylvania. They were driving in a rental car along a rather deserted highway. It was late, and raining very hard. Bob could barely see 20 feet in front of the car. Suddenly the car skids out of control! Bob attempts to control the car, but to no avail! The car swerves and smashes into a tree. Moments later, Bob shakes his head to clear the fog. Dazed, he looks over at the passenger seat and sees his wife unconscious, with her head bleeding! Despite the rain and unfamiliar countryside, Bob knows he

has to carry her to the nearest phone.

Bob carefully picks his wife up and begins trudging down the road. After a short while, he sees a light. He heads towards the light, which is coming from an old, large house. He approaches the door and knocks.

A minute passes. A small, hunched man opens the door. Bob immediately blurts, "Hello, my name is Bob Hill, and this is my wife Betty. We've been in a terrible accident, and my wife has been seriously hurt. Can I please use your phone?"

"I'm sorry," replied the hunchback, "but we don't have a phone. My master is a Doctor; come in and I will get him!"

Bob brings his wife in. An elegant man comes down the stairs. "I'm afraid my assistant may have misled you. I am not a medical doctor; I am a scientist. However, it is many miles to the nearest clinic, and I have had a basic medical training. I will see what I can do. Igor, bring them down to the laboratory."

With that, Igor picks up Betty and carries her downstairs, with Bob following closely. Igor places Betty on a table in the lab. Bob collapses from exhaustion and his own injuries, so Igor places Bob on an adjoining table.

After a brief examination, Igor's master looks worried. "Things are serious, Igor, prepare a transfusion." Igor and his master work feverishly, but to no avail. Bob and Betty Hill are no more.

The Hills' deaths upset Igor's master greatly. Wearily, he climbs the steps to his conservatory, which houses his grand piano. For it is here he has always found solace. He begins to play, and a stirring, almost haunting, melody fills the house.

Meanwhile, Igor is still in the lab tidying up. His eyes catch movement, and he notices the fingers on Betty's hand twitch. Stunned, he watches as Bob's arm begins to rise! He is further amazed as Betty sits straight up!

Unable to contain himself, he dashes up the stairs to the conservatory. He bursts in and shouts to his master:

"Master, Master! ...The Hills are alive with the sound of music!"

10. Three contractors were visiting a tourist attraction on the same

day. One was from New York, another from Texas, and the third from Florida.

At the end of the tour, the guard asked them what they did for a living. When they all replied they were contractors, the guard said, "Hey, we need one of the rear fences redone. Why don't you guys take a look at it and give me a bid?" So, to the back fence they all went to check it out. First to step up was the Florida contractor. He took out his tape measure and pencil, did some measuring and said, "Well, I figure the job will run about $900. $400 for materials, $400 for my crew, and $100 profit for me."

Next was the Texas contractor. He also took out his tape measure and pencil, did some quick figuring and said, "Looks like I can do this job for $700. $300 for materials, $300 for my crew, and $100 profit for me."

Without so much as moving, the New York contractor said, "$2,700." The guard, incredulous, looked at him and said, "You didn't even measure like the other guys! How did you come up with such a high figure?" "Easy," he said. "$1,000 for me, $1,000 for you and we hire the guy from Texas."

11. An usher noticed a man stretched across three seats in a movie theater. "Sorry, sir, but you're allowed only one seat." The man moaned but did not move. "Sir," continued the usher, "if you don't move, I'll have to call the manager." Again the man moaned but did not move. The manager then tried to get the man to move but had to call the police. "OK, buddy, what's your name?" asked the cop. "Joe," the man muttered. "And where are you from, Joe?" "The balcony!"

12. Why Men Can't Win
- If you work too hard, there is never any time for her.
- If you don't work enough, you're a good-for-nothing bum.
- If she has a boring repetitive job with low pay, it's exploitation.
- If you have a boring repetitive job with low pay, you should get off your butt and find something better.
- If you get a promotion ahead of her, it's favoritism.

♥ If she gets a job ahead of you, it's equal opportunity.
♥ If you mention how nice she looks, it's sexual harassment.
♥ If you keep quiet, it's male indifference.
♥ If you cry, you're a wimp.
♥ If you don't, you're insensitive.
♥ If you make a decision without consulting her, you're a chauvinist.
♥ If she makes a decision without consulting you, she's a liberated woman.
♥ If you ask her to do something she doesn't enjoy, that's domination.
♥ If she asks you, it's a favor.
♥ If you try to keep yourself in shape, you're vain.
♥ If you don't, you're a slob.
♥ If you buy her flowers, you're after something.
♥ If you don't, you're not thoughtful.
♥ If you're proud of your achievements, you're an egotist.
♥ If you're not, you're not ambitious.
♥ If she has a headache, she's tired.
♥ If you have a headache, you don't love her anymore.

13. A new Mercedes owner was out on an interstate for a nice evening drive. The top was down, the breeze was blowing through what was left of his hair and he decided to open her up.

As the needle jumped up to 80mph he suddenly saw a flashing red and blue light behind him. "There ain't no way they can catch a Mercedes," he thought to himself and opened her up further. The needle hit 90, 100, 110 and finally 120 with the lights still behind him.

"What in the world am I doing?" he thought and pulled over. The cop came up to him, took his license without a word, and examined it and the car. "I've had a tough shift and this is my last pull-over. I don't feel like more paperwork so if you can give me an excuse for your driving that I haven't heard before, you can go!"

He said, "Last week my wife ran off with a cop, and I was afraid you were trying to give her back!" "On your way," said the officer.

14. A man on his way home from work at the Pentagon came to a dead halt in traffic and thought to himself, "Wow, this traffic seems worse than usual. Nothing's even moving." He notices a police officer walking back and forth between the lines of cars so he rolls down his window and asks, "Excuse me, Officer, what's the hold up?" The Officer replies, "The President just found out Starr has delivered another report to the Congress and he's all depressed. He stopped his motorcade in the middle of the Beltway and he's threatening to douse himself in gasoline and set himself on fire. He says his family hates him and he doesn't have the $33.5 million he owes his lawyers. I'm walking around taking up a collection for him."
"Oh really? How much have you collected so far?"
"I've got a lot of folks still siphoning; but right now I have about three hundred gallons."

15. Mahatma Ghandi walked barefoot everywhere, to the point that his feet became quite thick and hard. He also was quite a spiritual person.
Even when he was not on a hunger strike, he did not eat much and became quite thin and frail. Furthermore, due to his diet, he ended up with very bad breath. Therefore, he came to be known as a . . .
"Super calloused fragile mystic plagued with halitosis."

Redneck Jokes
1. Subject: You Know You're A Redneck

ARKANSAS DRIVER'S LICENSE APPLICATION
   Last name: _____

   First name: (Check appropriate box)

[_] Billy-Bob   [_] Bobby-Sue
[_] Billy-Joe   [_] Bobby-Jo
[_] Billy-Ray   [_] Bobby-Ann
[_] Billy-Sue   [_] Bobby-Lee
[_] Billy-Mae   [_] Bobby-Ellen
[_] Billy-Jack   [_] Bobby-Beth
[_] Ann Sue   [_] Billy-Roscoe
   Age: ____ (if unsure, guess)
   Sex: ____ M ____ F ____ Not sure
   Shoe Size: ____ Left ____ Right
   Occupation:
[_] Farmer   [_] Mechanic
[_] Hair Dresser   [_] Waitress
[_] Un-employed   [_] Dirty Politician
   Spouse's Name: _____
   2nd Spouse's Name: _____
   3rd Spouse's Name: _____
   Lover's Name: _____
   2nd Lover's Name: _____
   Relationship with spouse:
[_] Sister   [_] Aunt
[_] Brother   [_] Uncle
[_] Mother   [_] Son
[_] Father   [_] Daughter
[_] Cousin   [_] Pet
   Number of children living in household: ___

Number of children living in shed: ___
Number of children that are yours: ___
Mother's Name: _____
Father's Name: _____ (If not sure, leave
    blank)
Education: 1 2 3 4 (Circle highest grade completed)
Do you [_] own or [_] rent your mobile home?
    (Check appropriate box)
Vehicles you own and where you keep them:
___ Total number of vehicles you own
___ Number of vehicles that still crank
___ Number of vehicles in front yard
___ Number of vehicles in back yard
___ Number of vehicles on cement blocks
Firearms you own and where you keep them:
____ truck   ____ kitchen
____ bedroom   ____ bathroom
____ shed
Model and year of your pickup: _____ 194_
Do you have a gun rack?
[_] Yes [_] No; If no, please explain:
Newspapers/magazines you subscribe to:
[_] The National Enquirer   [_] The Globe
[_] TV Guide   [_] Soap Opera Digest
[_] Rifle and Shotgun
___ Number of times you've seen a UFO
___ Number of times you've seen Elvis
___ Number of times you've seen Elvis in a UFO
How often do you bathe:
[_] Weekly
[_] Monthly
[_] Not Applicable
How many teeth?___
Color of teeth:
[_] Yellow   [_] Brownish-Yellow
[_] Brown   [_] Black
[_] N/A

Brand of chewing tobacco you prefer:
[_] Red-Man
How far is your home from a paved road?
[_] 1 mile
[_] 2 miles
[_] don't know

2. A fella walked into a bar and sat down by a woman. He said, 'Howdy, little darling. My name is Billy Bob Reynolds." She replied, "Why, hello, Billy Bob. When did you get here from Texas?" Billy Bob said, "How'd you know I'm from Texas?" The gal said, "Well, you said your name is Billy Bob and you called me Little Darling and you are so tall." "You're wrong about one thing. I'm not tall." He laughed. "You look tall sitting up there." she replied. "Oh," he said, "That's just because I'm sittin' on my wallet!"

3. Not to long ago a cowboy I know had a near death experience that has changed him forever. He was horseback riding, and everything was going fine until the horse started bouncing out of control. He tried with all his might to hang on, but was thrown off. His foot became caught in the stirrup. He fell head first to the ground and his head continued to bounce harder as the horse did not stop or even slow down. Just when things were looking their worst, as he was giving up hope and about to lose consciousness, there was a miracle: The K-Mart manager came and unplugged it.

4. Billy Joe and Billy Ray went to the big city to get jobs. They had been friends since they were kids, so they decided to apply at the same firm. They had finished filling out the applications and were waiting to see the owner. Billy Ray was called in first.

The owner was a stout man, with a weathered face and a scar above his right eye. He also had the distinguishing feature of having no ears, just two tiny holes in the sides of his head. The man ordered Billy Ray to sit down. He leaned across the desk and moved his cigar to the corner of his mouth. He growled at Billy Ray "This is a tough business. You have to be on your toes, keen, observant. Look around the room and tell me what you notice!" Billy Ray looked at the polished glass, chrome furniture, and large bar. He looked at the owner and said "You ain't got no ears!" The owner jumped out of his chair, grabbed Billy Ray by the neck and threw him out of his office.

Billy Joe saw Billy Ray come flying out the door and went over to help his friend up. "What happened?" Billy Joe told him, "What ever you do - don't talk about his ears!" Just then, the intercom buzzed and the secretary told Billy Joe he could go in.

Once again the owner ordered Billy Joe to sit down. He leaned across the desk and moved his cigar to the corner of his mouth. He growled at Billy Joe "This is a tough business. You have to be on your toes, keen, observant. Look around the room and tell me what you notice!"

Billy Joe looked at the polished glass, chrome furniture, and large bar. He looked at the owner and said "You wear contacts!"

The owner stood up in amazement. "That's awesome perception! How could you tell that from way over there?"

"Its obvious" said Billy Joe "You can't wear glasses, you ain't got no ears!"

5. Aggie Medical Terminology:
   Artery - the study of fine paintings;
   Benign - what you be after you be eight;
   Cesarean Section - a district in Rome;
   Coma - a punctuation mark;
   Colic - a sheep dog;
   Congenital - friendly;
   Dilate - to live longer;
   Fester - quicker;
   GI Series - baseball game between teams of soldiers';
   Morbid - a higher bid;
   Nitrate - lower than the day rate;
   Node - was aware of;
   Urine - opposite of yours out;

Protein - in favor of a young team;
Tumor - an extra pair.

6. You may be a redneck if:
You barbecue Spam on the grill.
Redman sends you a Christmas card.
Your brother-in-law is your uncle.
You bought a VCR solely for the purpose of taping wrestling while you are at work.
You prominently display a gift you got at Graceland.
You call your boss "Dude."
You have been fired from a construction job because of your appearance.
You need one more hole punched in your card to get a freebie at the House of Tattoos.
Your father encouraged you to quit school because Larry had an opening on the lube rack.
You need an estimate from your barber before you get a haircut.
Your wife has a beer belly and you find it attractive.

7. IDIOTS DELIGHTS:
Sign in a gas station: Coke -- 49 cents. Two for a dollar.
I was signing the receipt for my credit card purchase when the clerk noticed I had never signed my name on the back of the credit card. She informed me she could not complete the transaction unless the card was signed. When I asked why, she explained it was necessary to compare the signature on the credit card with the signature I just signed on the receipt.
So I signed the credit card in front of her. She carefully compared that signature to the one I signed on the receipt. As luck would have it, they matched.

IDIOTS & GEOGRAPHY
After interviewing a particularly short-spoken job candidate, I described the person to my boss as rather monosyllabic. My boss said, "Really? Where is Monosyllabia?" Thinking he was just kid-

ding, I played along and said it was just south of Elbonia. He replied, "Oh, you mean over by Croatia?"

IDIOTS IN THE NEIGHBORHOOD

I live in a semi-rural area. We recently had a new neighbor call the local township administrative office to request the removal of the Deer Crossing sign on our road. The reason: Many deer were being hit by cars and he no longer wanted them to cross there.

IDIOTS & COMPUTERS

My neighbor works in the operations department in the central office of a large bank. Employees in the field call him when they have problems with their computers. One night he got a call from a woman in one of the branch banks who had this question: "I've got smoke coming from the back of my terminal. Do you guys have a fire downtown?"

IDIOTS ARE EASY TO PLEASE

I was sitting in my science class, when the teacher commented the next day would be the shortest day of the year. My lab partner became visibly excited, cheering and clapping. I explained to her that the amount of daylight changes, not the actual amount of time. Needless to say, she was very disappointed.

IDIOTS IN FOOD SERVICE

My daughter went to a local Taco Bell and ordered a taco. She asked the individual behind the counter for "minimal lettuce ". He said he was sorry, but they only had iceberg.

AN IDIOT'S IDIOT

Police in Radnor, Pennsylvania, interrogated a suspect by placing a metal colander on his head and connecting it with wires to a photo copy machine. The message "He's lying." was placed in the copier, and police pressed the copy button each time they thought the suspect was telling a lie. Believing the "lie detector" was working; the suspect confessed.

8. Subject: Top Ten ways to tell if a redneck has been working at a computer:

10) The motherboard is up on blocks.

9) Outgoing faxes have tobacco stains on them.

8) The six front keys have rotted out.

7) The extra RAM slots have Dodge truck parts installed in them.

6) The numeric key pad only goes up to six.

5) The password is "Bubba".

4) There is a gun rack mounted on the monitor.

3) There is a Skoal can in the CD ROM drive.

2) The keyboard is camouflaged.

1) The mouse is referred to as a "critter".

9. You may be a redneck if -

You consider a six-pack and a bug zapper quality entertainment.

Your Junior/Senior Prom had a daycare.

The primary color of your car is Bondo.

The directions to your house include "Turn off the paved road."

Your dog and your wallet are both on chains.

Your kids are going hungry tonight because you just had to have those Yosemite Sam mud flaps.

You owe the taxidermist more than your annual income.

You have lost at least one tooth opening a beer bottle.

Jack Daniels makes your list of most admired people.

You have a hefty bag on the passenger side window of your car.

10. A young man was looking for the perfect woman. He had almost given up when he sat beside what appeared to him to be the perfect woman. He began talking to her and asked, "What do you like in a man?"

The woman replied, "I like the Indian man because he is tall, dark and handsome. I also like the Jewish man for his intelligence and his wealth. But I really like the good ole boy for his masculinity."

Then she asked, "By the way, what is your name?" To this question the young man proudly answered, "Geronimo Goldberg, but my friends call me 'Bubba.'

11. Etiquette for men
DINING OUT
1. When decanting wine, make sure you tilt the paper cup, and pour slowly so as not to "bruise" the fruit of the vine.
2. If drinking directly from the bottle, always hold it with your fingers covering the label.

ENTERTAINING IN YOUR HOME
1. A centerpiece for the table should never be anything prepared by a taxidermist.
2. Do not allow the dog to eat at the table...no matter how good his manners are.

PERSONAL HYGIENE
1. While ears need to be cleaned regularly, this is a job that should be done in private using one's OWN truck keys.
2. Proper use of toiletries can forestall bathing for several days. However, if you live alone, deodorant is a waste of good money.
3. Dirt and grease under the fingernails is a social no-no, as they tend to detract from a woman's jewelry and alter the taste of finger foods.

DATING (Outside the Family)
1.Always offer to bait your date's hook, especially on the first date.
2.Be aggressive. Let her know you're interested: "I've been wanting to go out with you since I read that stuff on the bathroom wall two years ago."
3. Establish with her parents what time she is expected back. Some will say 10:00 PM; Others might say "Monday." If the latter is the answer, it is the man's responsibility to get her to school on time.

THEATER ETIQUETTE
1. Crying babies should be taken to the lobby and picked up imme-

diately after the movie has ended.
2. Refrain from talking to characters on the screen. Tests have proven they can't hear you.

WEDDINGS
1. Livestock, usually, is a poor choice for a wedding gift.
2. Kissing the bride for more than 5 seconds may get you shot.
3. For the groom, at least, rent a tux. A leisure suit with a cummerbund and a clean bowling shirt can create a tacky appearance.
4. Though uncomfortable, say "yes" to socks and shoes for this special occasion.

DRIVING ETIQUETTE
1. Dim your headlights for approaching vehicles; even if the gun is loaded, and the deer is in sight.
2. When approaching a four-way stop, the vehicle with the largest tires always has the right of way.
3. Never tow another car using panty hose and duct tape.
4. When sending your wife down the road with a gas can, it is impolite to ask her to bring back beer.
5. Never relieve yourself from a moving vehicle, especially when driving.
6. Do not lay rubber while traveling in a funeral procession.

TIPS FOR ALL OCCASIONS
1. Never take a beer to a job interview.
2. Always identify people in your yard before shooting at them.
3. It's considered tacky to take a cooler to church.
4. If you have to vacuum the bed, it is time to change the sheets.
5. Even if you're certain you are included in the will, it is still considered tacky to drive a U-Haul to the funeral home.

12. Two rednecks, Bubba and Earl, were driving down the road drinking a couple of bottles of Bud. The passenger, Bubba, said, "Lookey thar up ahead, Earl, it's a poll-ice roadblock! We're gonna get busted fer drinkin' these here beers!"

"Don't worry, Bubba," Earl said, "We'll just pull over and finish drinkin' these beers. Then peel off the label and stick it on our foreheads, and throw the bottles under the seat."

"What fer?" asked Bubba.

" Just let me do the talkin', OK?" said Earl.

When they finished their beers, threw the empty bottles under the seat, and each put a label on their forehead. When they reached the roadblock, the sheriff said, "You boys been drinkin'?"

"No, sir," said Earl. "We're on the patch."

13. 5 STAGES OF DRUNKENNESS

Stage 1 - SMART

This is when you suddenly become an expert on every subject in the known Universe. You know you know everything and want to pass on your knowledge to anyone who will listen. At this stage you are always RIGHT. And of course the person you are talking to is very WRONG. This makes for an interesting argument when both parties are SMART.

Stage 2 - GOOD LOOKING

This is when you realize you are the BEST LOOKING person in the entire bar and people fancy you. You can go up to a perfect stranger knowing they fancy you and really want to talk to you. Bear in mind you are still SMART, so you can talk to this person about any subject under the sun.

Stage 3 - RICH

This is when you suddenly become the richest person in the world. You can buy drinks for the entire bar because you have an armored truck full of money parked behind the bar. You can also make bets at this stage, because of course, you are still SMART, so naturally you win all your bets. It doesn't matter how much you bet 'cos you are RICH. You will also buy drinks for everyone that you fancy, because now you are the BEST LOOKING person in the world.

Stage 4 - BULLET PROOF

You are now ready to pick fights with anyone and everyone specially those with whom you have been betting or arguing. This is because nothing can hurt you. At this point you can also go up to the partners of the people who you fancy and challenge to a battle of wits or money. You have no fear of losing this battle because you are SMART, you are RICH and heck, you're BETTER LOOKING than they are anyway!

Stage 5 - INVISIBLE

This is the Final Stage of Drunkenness. At this point you can do anything because NO ONE CAN SEE YOU. You dance on a table to impress the people who you fancy because the rest of the people in the room cannot see you. You are also invisible to the person who wants to fight you. You can walk through the street singing at the top of your lungs because no one can see or hear you and because you're still SMART you know all the words.

14. Colorado Springs: A guy walked into a little corner store with a shot gun and demanded all the cash from the cash drawer. After the cashier put the cash in a bag, the robber saw a bottle of scotch he wanted behind the counter on the shelf. He told the cashier to put it in the bag as well, but he refused and said "Because I don't believe you are over 21."
The robber said he was, but the clerk still refused to give it to him because he didn't believe him. At this point the robber took his drivers license out of his wallet and gave it to the clerk. The clerk looked it over, and agreed the man was in fact over 21 and he put the scotch in the bag. The robber then ran from the store with his loot. The cashier promptly called the police and gave the name and address of the robber he got off the license. They arrested the robber two hours later.

15. A woman was reporting her car as stolen, and mentioned there was a car phone in it. The policeman taking the report called the phone and told the guy that answered he had read the ad in the newspaper and wanted to buy the car. They arranged to meet, and the thief was arrested.

16. A true story out of San Francisco: A man, wanting to rob a downtown Bank of America, walked into the branch and wrote

"this iz a stikkup. Put all your muny in this bag." While standing in line, waiting to give his note to the teller, he began to worry someone had seen him write the note and might call the police before he reached the teller window. So he left the Bank of America and crossed the street to Wells Fargo. After waiting a few minutes in line, he handed his note to the Wells Fargo teller. She read it and, surmising from his spelling errors he was not the brightest light in the harbor, told him she could not accept his stickup note because it was written on a Bank of America deposit slip and he would either have to fill out a Wells Fargo deposit slip or go back to Bank of America. Looking somewhat defeated, the man said "OK" and left. The Wells Fargo teller then called the police who arrested the man a few minutes later, as he was waiting in line back at Bank of America.

17. A motorist was unknowingly caught in an automated speed trap that measured his speed using radar and photographed his car. He later received in the mail a ticket for $40 and a photo of his car. Instead of payment, he sent the police department a photograph of $40. Several days later, he received a letter from the police that contained another picture...of handcuffs. The motorist promptly sent the money for the fine.

18. A drug possession defendant on trial in March in Pontiac, Michigan, said he had been searched without a warrant. The prosecutor said the officer didn't need a warrant because a "bulge" in his jacket could have been a gun. Nonsense, said the defendant, who happened to be wearing the same jacket that day in court. He handed it over so the judge could see it. The judge discovered a packet of cocaine in the pocket and laughed so hard he required a five minute recess to compose himself.

19. OKC: A man was on trial for the armed robbery of a convenience store in a district court when he fired his lawyer. The Assistant District Attorney said the defendant was doing a fair job of defending himself until the store manager testified the man was the

robber. The "man" jumped up, accused the woman of lying and then said, "I should of blown your (expletive) head off." The defendant paused, then quickly added, "if I'd been the one that was there." The jury took 20 minutes to convict him and recommended a 30-year sentence.

20. Detroit: A 21-year-old man walked up to two patrol officers who were showing their squad car computer equipment to children in a Detroit neighborhood. When he asked how the system worked, the officer asked him for identification. The man gave them his drivers license, they entered it into the computer, and moments later they arrested him because information on the screen showed he was wanted for a two-year-old armed robbery in St. Louis, Missouri.

21. A pair of Michigan robbers entered a record shop nervously waving revolvers. The first one shouted, "Nobody move!" When his partner moved, the startled first bandit shot him.

22. Cigars and Insurance
A Charlotte, NC, man having purchased a case of very rare, very expensive cigars, insured them against fire among other things. Within a month, having smoked his entire stockpile of cigars and without having made even his first premium payment on the policy, the man filed a claim against the insurance company. In his claim, the man stated the cigars were lost "in a series of small fires." The insurance company refused to pay, citing the obvious reason the man had consumed the cigars in the normal fashion. The man sued.... and won. In delivering the ruling the judge, agreeing the claim was frivolous, stated nevertheless the man held a policy from the company in which it had warranted that the cigars were insurable and also guaranteed it would insure against fire, without defining what it considered to be "unacceptable fire," and was obligated to pay the claim.

Rather than endure a lengthy and costly appeal process the insurance company accepted the ruling and paid the man $15,000 for the rare cigars he lost in "the fires." After the man cashed the check, however, the company had him arrested on 24 counts of arson. With his own insurance claim and testimony from the previous case being used against him, the man was convicted of intentionally burning his insured property and sentenced to 24 months in jail and a $24,000 fine.

23. The local sheriff was looking for a deputy, so Gomer - who was not exactly the sharpest nail in the bucket went in to try out for the job. "Okay," the sheriff drawled, "Gomer, what is 1 and 1?" "11" he replied.
The sheriff thought to himself, "That's not what I meant, but he's right." "What two days of the week start with the letter 'T'?" "Today and tomorrow." He was again surprised that Gomer supplied a correct answer that he had never thought of himself.
"Now Gomer, listen carefully: Who killed Abraham Lincoln?"
Gomer looked a little surprised himself, then thought really hard for a minute and finally admitted, "I don't know."
"Well, why don't you go home and work on that one for a while?"
So, Gomer wandered over to the drive-in where his pals were waiting to hear the results of the interview. Gomer was exultant. "It went great! First day on the job and I'm already working on a murder case!"

24. A Texan bought a ticket and wins the lottery. He goes to Austin to claim it and the lottery official verifies his ticket number. The Texas says "I want my $20 million." The lottery official replied, "No sir. It doesn't work that way. We give you a million today and then you'll get the rest spread out over the next 19 years." The Texas said "Oh , no. I want all my money right now. I won it and I want it." Again the lottery official explained that he would only get a million that day and a million a year for the next 19 years. The Texan, now furious with the man, screams out, "Look, I want my money! If you're not going to give me my $20 million right now, then I want my dollar back!"

25. The Association of Southern Schools has decided to pursue

some of the seemingly endless taxpayer dollar pipeline through Washington designating Southern slang, or "Hickbonics," as a language to be taught in all Southern schools. A speaker of this language would be a Hickophone.

The following are excerpts from the Hickbonics/English dictionary:

HEIDI - (noun) -Greeting.

HIRE YEW - Complete sentence. Remainder of greeting. Usage: Heidi, Hire yew?"

BARD - (verb) - Past tense of the infinitive "to borrow."
Usage: "My brother bard my pickup truck."

JAWJUH - (noun) - The State north of Florida. Capitol is Lanner.
Usage: "My brother from Jawjuh bard my pickup truck."

TUCK - (verb) - took
Usage: "My brother from Jawjuh bard my pickup truck and tuck it to Lanner."

BAMMER - (noun) - The State west of Jawjuh. Capitol is Berminhayum.
Usage: "A tornader jes went through Bammer an' left 20,000,000 in improvements."

MUNTS - (noun) - A calendar division.
Usage: "My brother from Jawjuh bard my pickup truck, and I ain't herd from him in munts."

THANK - (verb) - Ability to cognitively process.
Usage: "Ah thank ah'll have a bare."

BARE - (noun) - An alcoholic beverage made of barley, hops, and yeast.
Usage: "Ah thank ah'll have a bare."

IGNERT - (adjective) - Not smart. See "Arkansas native."
Usage: "Them bammer boys sure are ignert!"

RANCH - (noun) - A tool used for tight'nin' bolts.
Usage: "I thank I left my ranch in the back of that pickup truck my brother from Jawjuh bard a few munts ago."

ALL - (noun) - A petroleum-based lubricant.
Usage: "I sure hope my brother from Jawjuh puts all in my pickup truck."

FAR - (noun) - A conflagration.
Usage: "If my brother from Jawjuh don't change the all in my pickup truck, that thing's gonna catch far."
TAR - (noun) - A rubber wheel.
Usage: "Gee, I hope that brother of mine from Jawjuh don't git a flat tar on my pickup truck."
TIRE - (noun) - A tall monument.
Usage: "Lord willin' and the creek don't rise, I sure do hope to see that Eiffel Tire in Paris sometime."
RETARD - (verb) - To stop working.
Usage: "My grampaw retard at age 65."
FAT - (noun), (verb) - a battle or combat; to engage in battle or combat.
Usage: "You younguns keep fat'n, 'n' ah'm gonna whup y'uh."
RATS - (noun) - Entitled power or privilege.
Usage: "We Southerners are willin' to fat for are rats."
FARN - (adjective) - Not domestic.
Usage: "I cuddint unnerstand a wurd he sed...must be from some farn country."
DID - (adjective) - Not alive.
Usage: "He's did, Jim."
EAR - (noun) - A colorless, odorless gas mostly consisting of oxygen.
Usage: "He cain't breathe...give 'im some ear!"
BOB WAR - (noun) - A sharp, twisted cable.
Usage: "Boy, stay away from that bob-war fence."
JEW HERE - (noun) and (verb) contraction.
Usage: "Jew here that my brother from Jawjuh got a job with that bob-war fence cump'ny?"
HAZE - a contraction.
Usage: "Is Bubba smart?"
"Nah...haze ignert. He ain't thanked but a minnit ' n 'is laf."
SEED - (verb) - past tense of "to see."
Usage: "I seed that cow was did right off."
VIEW - contraction: (verb) and pronoun.
Usage: "I ain't never seed New York City... view?"
GUBMINT - (noun) - A bureaucratic institution.

Usage: "Them gubmint boys shore is ignert."

26. I think there are SOME people I know that actually need these warning labels! The FDA is considering 13 additional warnings on beer and alcohol bottles, such as:

13. WARNING: consumption of alcohol may make you think you are whispering when you are not.

12. WARNING: consumption of alcohol is a major factor in dancing like an idiot.

11. WARNING: consumption of alcohol may cause you to tell the same boring story over and over again until your friends want to SMASH YOUR HEAD IN.

10. WARNING: consumption of alcohol may cause you to thay shings like thish.

9. WARNING: consumption of alcohol may lead you to believe that ex-lovers are really dying for you to telephone them at 4 in the morning.

8. WARNING: consumption of alcohol may leave you wondering what the hell happened to your pants.

7. WARNING: consumption of alcohol may cause you to roll over in the morning and see something really scary (whose species and or name you can't remember).

6. WARNING: consumption of alcohol is the leading cause of inexplicable rug burns on the forehead.

5. WARNING: consumption of alcohol may create the illusion that you are tougher, handsomer and smarter than some really, really big guy named Bob.

4. WARNING: consumption of alcohol may lead you to believe you are invisible.

3. WARNING: consumption of alcohol may lead you to think people are laughing WITH you.

2. WARNING: Consumption of alcohol may cause an influx in the time-space continuum, whereby small (and sometimes large) gaps of time may seem to literally "disappear."

1. WARNING: Consumption of alcohol may actually CAUSE

pregnancy.

27. Redneck Family Tree

Many, many years ago
When I was twenty-three,
I got married to a widow
Who was pretty as could be.

This widow had a daughter
Who had hair of red
My father fell in love with her,
And soon the two were wed.

This made my dad my son-in-law
And changed my very life.
My daughter was my mother,
For she was my father's wife.

To complicate the matters worse,
Although it brought me joy,
I soon became the father
Of a bouncing baby boy.

My little baby then became
A brother-in-law to dad.
And so became my uncle,
Though it made me very sad.

For if he was my uncle,
Then that also made him brother
To the widow's grown-up daughter
Who, of course was my step-mother.

Father's wife then had a son,
Who kept them on the run.
And he became my grandson,
For he was my daughter's son.

My wife is now my mother's mom.
And it surely makes me blue.
Because, although she is my wife,
She is my grandma too.

If my wife is my grandmother,
Then I am her grandchild.
And every time I think of it,
It simply drives me wild.

For now I have become
The strangest case you ever saw.
As the husband of my grandmother,
I am my own grandpa!

☺

Tech Jokes

These jokes are really for computer users. May not be funny to non-users.

1. To: Tech Support

Last year I upgraded Girlfriend 1.0 to Wife 1.0 and noticed the new program began unexpected child processing that took up a lot of space and valuable resources. No mention of this phenomenon was included in the product brochure. In addition, Wife 1.0 installs itself into all other programs and launches during system initialization where it monitors all other system activity.

Applications such as FISHING 10.3 and TENNIS 2.5 no longer run, crashing the system whenever selected. I can not seem to purge Wife 1.0 from my system. I am thinking about going back to Girlfriend 1.0 but un-install does not work on this program. Can you help me?

Jonathan Powell

To: Mr. Powell

This is a very common problem men complain about but it is mostly due to a primary misconception. Many men upgrade from Girlfriend 1.0 to Wife 1.0 with the idea that Wife 1.0 is merely a "UTILITIES & ENTERTAINMENT" program. Wife 1.0 is an OPERATING SYSTEM and designed by its creator to run everything. It is impossible to un-install, delete, or purge the program from the system once installed. You can not go back to Girlfriend 1.0 because Wife 1.0 is not designed to do this. Some have tried to install Girlfriend 2.0 or Wife 2.0 but end up with more problems than original system. Look in your manual under Warnings -

Alimony/Child Support. I recommend you keep Wife 1.0 and just deal with the situation. Having Wife 1.0 installed myself, I might also suggest you read the entire section regarding General Protection Faults (GPFs). You must assume all responsibility for faults and problems that might occur. The best course of action will be to push apologize button then reset button as soon as lock-up occurs.

System will run smooth as long as you take the blame for all GPFs. Wife 1.0 is a great program but is very high maintenance.
Tech Support

2. Customer: "Your sound card is defective and I want a new one."
Tech Support: "What seems to be the problem?"
Customer: "The balance is backwards. The left channel is coming out of the right speaker and the right channel is coming out the left. It's defective."
Tech Support: "You can solve the problem by moving the left speaker to the right side of the machine and vice versa."
Customer:(sputter) (click)
Tech Support: (snicker)

3. Customer: "I'd like to return this scanner."
Store Clerk: "Excuse me?" Customer: "This scanner I bought. I paid eighty dollars for this scanner, and it doesn't work!"
Store Clerk: "Uh . . . sir, that's a trackball."
Customer: "No, it isn't. It says 600 dpi tracking resolution right here!"

4. Got a call from a woman said her laser printer was having problems: the bottom half of her printed sheets were coming out blurry. It seemed strange the printer was smearing only the bottom half. I walked her through the basics, then came over and printed out a test sheet. It printed fine. I asked her to print a sheet, so she sent a job to the printer. As the paper started coming out, she yanked it out and showed it to me. I told her to WAIT until the paper came out on its own. Problem solved.

5. I had been doing Tech Support for Hewlett-Packard's DeskJet division for about a month when I had a customer call with a problem I just couldn't solve. She could not print yellow. All the other colors would print fine, which truly baffled me because the only true colors are cyan, magenta, and yellow. For instance, green is a combination of cyan and yellow, but green printed fine. Every color

of the rainbow printed fine except for yellow.

I had the customer change ink cartridges. I had the customer delete and reinstall the drivers. Nothing worked. I asked my co-workers for help; they offered no new ideas. After over two hours of troubleshooting, I was about to tell the customer to send the printer in to us for repair when she asked quietly, "Should I try printing on a piece of white paper instead of this yellow construction paper?"

6. A man attempting to set up his new printer called the printer's tech support number, complaining about the error message: "Can't find the printer."

On the phone, the man said he even held the printer up in front of the screen, but the computer still couldn't find it!

7. Customer: "Hello? I'm trying to dial in. I installed the software okay, and it dialed fine. I could hear that. Then I could hear the two computers connecting. But then the sound all stopped, so I picked up the phone to see if they were still connected, and I got the message, 'No Carrier' on my screen. What's wrong?"

8. An unfailingly polite lady called to ask for help with a Windows installation had gone terribly wrong.

Customer: "I brought my Windows disks from work to install them on my home computer." (Training stresses we are "not the Soft-ware Police, "so I let the little act of piracy slide.)

Tech Support: "Umm-hmm. What happened?"

Customer: "As I put each disk in it turns out they weren't initialized."

Tech Support: "Do you remember the message exactly, ma'am?"

Customer: (proudly) "I wrote it down. 'This is not a Macintosh disk. Would you like to initialize it'?"

Tech Support: "Er, what happened next?"

Customer: "After they were initialized all the disks appeared to be blank. And now I brought them back to work, and I can't read them in the A: drive; the PC wants to format them. And this is our only set of Windows disks for the whole office. Did I do something wrong?"

9. For a computer programming class, I sat directly across from someone with our computers facing away from each other. A few minutes into the class, she got up to leave the room. I reached between our computers and switched the inputs for the keyboards. She came back and started typing and immediately got a distressed look on her face.

She called the teacher over and explained no matter what she typed, nothing would happen. The teacher tried everything. By this time I was hiding behind my monitor and quaking red-faced. I started to type, "Leave me alone!"

They both jumped back, silenced.

"What the . . . " the teacher said.

I typed, "I said leave me alone!"

The kid got real upset. "I didn't do anything to it, I swear!"

It was all I could do to keep from laughing out loud. The conversation between them and HAL 2000 went on for an amazing five minutes.

Me: "Don't touch me!"

Her: "I'm sorry, I didn't mean to hit your keys that hard."

Me: "Who do you think you are anyway?!" Etc. Finally, I couldn't contain myself any longer and fell out of my chair laughing. After they had realized what I had done, they both turned beet red.

Funny, I never got more than a C- in that class.

10. I have a friend who just bought a computer and was instructed to load a program by typing "A:" and then the name of the program. My friend told me it would not work because his keyboard was no good. He said he couldn't type the "dot over dot thingie" and every time he tried to type the "dot over dot thingie" he kept getting the "dot over comma thingie" no matter how careful he was to press only on the very top of the key. When I taught him about the shift key, he thought I was a genius.

11. This guy calls in to complain he gets an "Access Denied" message every time he logs in. It turned out he was typing his user name and password in capital letters.

Tech Support: "OK, let's try once more, but use lower case letters."

Customer: "Uh, I only have capital letters on my keyboard."

12.Top ten reasons why a dog can't use the computer:

#10. He's distracted by cats chasing his mouse...

#9. SIT and STAY were hard enough; CUT and PASTE are out of the question.

#8. Saliva-coated floppy disks refuse to work.

#7. Three words: carpal paw syndrome.

#6. Involuntary tail wagging is a dead give-away he's browsing www.purina.com instead of working.

#5. The fire hydrant icon is simply too frustrating.

#4. He can't help attacking the screen when he hears "You've Got Mail"

#3. It's too messy to "mark" every Web site he visits.

#2. The FETCH command isn't available on all platforms. and (drum roll)...

#1. He can't stick his head out of Windows 95.

13. WHAT IF PEOPLE BOUGHT CARS LIKE THEY BOUGHT COMPUTERS?

General Motors doesn't have a "help line" for people who don't Know how to drive, because people don't buy cars like they buy computers but imagine if they did . . .

HELPLINE: "General Motors Helpline, how can I help you?"

CUSTOMER: "I got in my car and closed the door, and nothing happened!"

HELPLINE: "Did you put the key in the ignition slot and turn it?"

CUSTOMER: "What's an ignition?"

HELPLINE: "It's a starter motor that draws current from your battery and turns over the engine."

CUSTOMER: "Ignition? Motor? Battery? Engine? How come I have to know all of these technical terms just to use my car?"

HELPLINE: "General Motors Helpline, how can I help you?"

CUSTOMER: "My car ran fine for a week, and now it won't go anywhere!"

HELPLINE: "Is the gas tank empty?"

CUSTOMER: "Huh? How do I know?"

HELPLINE: "There's a little gauge on the front panel, with a needle, and markings from 'E' to 'F.' Where is the needle pointing?"

CUSTOMER: "It's pointing to 'E.' What does that mean?"

HELPLINE: "It means you have to visit a gasoline vendor, and purchase some more gasoline. You can install it yourself, or pay the vendor to install it for you."

CUSTOMER: "What!? I paid $12,000 for this car! Now you tell me I have to keep buying more components? I want a car that comes with everything built in!"

HELPLINE: "General Motors Helpline, how can I help you?"

CUSTOMER: "Your car sucks!"

HELPLINE: "What's wrong?"

CUSTOMER: "It crashed, that's what went wrong!"

HELPLINE: "What were you doing?"

CUSTOMER: "I wanted to run faster, so I pushed the accelerator pedal all the way to the floor. It worked for a while, and then it crashed -- and now it won't start!"

HELPLINE: "It's your responsibility if you misuse the product. What do you expect us to do about it?"

CUSTOMER: "I want you to send me one of the latest versions that doesn't crash anymore!"

HELPLINE: "General Motors Helpline, how can I help you?"

CUSTOMER: "Hi! I just bought my first car, and I chose your car because it has automatic transmission, cruise control, power steering, power brakes, and power door locks."

HELPLINE: "Thanks for buying our car. How can I help you?"

CUSTOMER: "How do I work it?"

HELPLINE: "Do you know how to drive?"

CUSTOMER: "Do I know how to what?"

HELPLINE: "Do you know how to drive?"

CUSTOMER: "I'm not a technical person! I just want to go places in my car!"

14. My friend was on duty in the main lab on a quiet afternoon. He noticed a young woman sitting in front of one of the workstations with her arms crossed across her chest and staring at the screen. After about 15 minutes he noticed she was still in the same position only now she was impatiently tapping her foot. He asked if she needed help and she replied, "It's about time! I pushed the F1 button over twenty minutes ago!"

15. WHERE DO YOU WANT TO GO TODAY?
At a recent computer expo (COMDEX), Bill Gates reportedly compared the computer industry with the auto industry and stated: "If GM had kept
up with technology like the computer industry has, we would all be driving twenty-five dollar cars that got 1000 miles to the gallon."
In response to Bill's comments, General Motors issued a press release
stating (by Mr. Welch himself): If GM had developed technology like
Microsoft, we would all be driving cars with the following characteristics:
1. For no reason whatsoever your car would crash twice a day.
2. Every time they repainted the lines on the road you would have to
buy a new car.
3. Occasionally your car would die on the freeway for no reason, and
you would just accept this, restart and drive on.
4. Occasionally, executing a maneuver such as a left turn, would cause your car to shut down and refuse to restart, in which case you would have to reinstall the engine.
5. Only one person at a time could use the car, unless you bought "Car95" or "CarNT". But then you would have to buy more seats.
6. Macintosh would make a car that was powered by the sun, reliable, five times as fast, and twice as easy to drive, but would only

run on five per cent of the roads.

7. The oil, water temperature and alternator warning lights would be replaced by a single "general car default" warning light.

8. New seats would force everyone to have the same size butt.

9. The airbag system would say "Are you sure?" before going off.

10. Occasionally, and for no reason whatsoever, your car would lock you out and refuse to let you in until you simultaneously lifted the door handle, turned the key, and grab hold of the radio antenna.

11. GM would require all car buyers to also purchase a deluxe set of Rand McNally road maps (now a GM subsidiary), even though they neither need them nor want them. Attempting to delete this option would Immediately cause the car's performance to diminish by 50% or more. Moreover, GM would become a target for investigation by the Justice Department.

12. Every time GM introduced a new model car buyers would have to learn how to drive all over again because none of the controls would operate in the same manner as the old car.

13. You'd press the "start" button to shut off the engine.

16. E-mail from a friend: "CanYouFixTheSpaceBarOnMyKeyboard?"

17. I saw a lady at work today putting a credit card into her floppy drive and pulling it out very quickly. I inquired as to what she was doing and she said she was shopping on the Internet, and they asked for a credit card number, so she was using the ATM "thingy."

18. I worked with an individual who plugged his power strip back into itself and for the life of him could not understand why his computer would not turn on.

19. 1st Person: "Do you know anything about this fax-machine?"
2nd Person: "A little. What's wrong?"
1st Person: "Well, I sent a fax, and the recipient called back to say all she received was a cover-sheet and a blank page. I tried it again, and the same thing happened."
2nd Person: "How did you load the sheet?"
1st Person: "It's a pretty sensitive memo, and I didn't want anyone else to read it by accident, so I folded it so only the recipient would

open it and read it."

20. My friend called his car insurance company to tell them to change his address from Texas to Vermont. The woman who took the call asked where Vermont was. As he tried to explain, she interrupted and said, "Look, I'm not stupid or anything, but what state is it in?"

21. I was in a car dealership a while ago when a large motorhome was towed into the garage. The front of the vehicle was in dire need of repair and the whole thing generally looked like an extra in "Twister." I asked the manager what had happened. He told me that the driver had set the cruise control, then went in back to make a sandwich.

22. I called a company and asked to speak to Bob. The person who answered said, "Bob is on vacation. Would you like to hold?"

23. The Baltimore Police Department, famous for its superior K-9 unit, was somewhat taken aback by a recent incident. Returning home from work, a woman had been shocked to find her house ransacked and burglarized. She telephoned the police at once and reported the crime. The police dispatcher broadcast the call on the channels, and a K-9 officer patrolling nearby was first on the scene. As he approached the house with his dog on a leash, the woman ran out on the porch, clapped a hand to her head and moaned, "I come home from work to find all my possessions stolen, I call the police for help, and what do they do? They send a blind policeman!"

Tombstone Jokes
(Not really dead jokes)

1. Epitaphs from real tombstones:

On the grave of Ezekial Aikle in East Dalhousie Cemetery, Nova Scotia:
Here lies
Ezekial Aikle
Age 102
The Good
Die Young.

In a London, England cemetery:
Ann Mann
Here lies Ann Mann,
Who lived an old maid
But died an old Mann.
Dec. 8, 1767

In a Ribbesford, England, cemetery:
Anna Wallace
The children of Israel wanted bread
And the Lord sent them manna,
Old clerk Wallace wanted a wife,
And the Devil sent him Anna.

Playing with names in a Ruidoso, New Mexico, cemetery:
Here lies
Johnny Yeast
Pardon me
For not rising.

Memory of an accident in a Uniontown, Pennsylvania cemetery:
Here lies the body

of Jonathan Blake
Stepped on the gas
Instead of the brake.

In a Silver City, Nevada, cemetery:
Here lays Butch,
We planted him raw.
He was quick on the trigger,
But slow on the draw.

A widow wrote this epitaph in a Vermont cemetery:
Sacred to the memory of my husband John Barnes
who died January 3, 1803
His comely young widow, aged 23, has
many qualifications of a good wife, and
yearns to be comforted.

A lawyer's epitaph in England:
Sir John Strange
Here lies an honest lawyer,
And that is Strange.

Someone determined to be anonymous in Stowe, Vermont:
I was somebody.
Who, is no business
Of yours.

Lester Moore was a Wells, Fargo Co. station agent for Naco, Arizona in the cowboy days of the 1880's. He's buried in the Boot Hill Cemetery in Tombstone, Arizona:
Here lies Lester Moore
Four slugs from a .44
No Les No More.

In a Georgia cemetery:
"I told you I was sick!"

John Penny's epitaph in the Wimborne, England, cemetery:
Reader if cash thou art
In want of any
Dig 4 feet deep
And thou wilt find a Penny.

On Margaret Daniels grave at Hollywood Cemetery, Richmond, Virginia:
She always said her feet were killing her
but nobody believed her.

In a cemetery in Hartscombe, England:
On the 22nd of June
- Jonathan Fiddle -
Went out of tune.

Anna Hopewell's grave in Enosburg Falls, Vermont has an epitaph that sounds like something from a Three Stooges movie:
Here lies the body of our Anna
Done to death by a banana
It wasn't the fruit that laid her low
But the skin of the thing that made her go.

More fun with names with Owen Moore in Battersea, London, England:
Gone away - Owin' more - Than he could pay.

Someone in Winslow, Maine didn't like Mr. Wood:
In Memory of Beza Wood
Departed this life
Nov. 2, 1837
Aged 45 yrs.
Here lies one Wood
Enclosed in wood
One Wood
Within another.

The outer wood
Is very good:
We cannot praise
The other.

On a grave from the 1880's in Nantucket, Massachusetts:
Under the sod and under the trees
Lies the body of Jonathan Pease.
He is not here, there's only the pod:
Pease shelled out and went to God.

The grave of Ellen Shannon in Girard, Pennsylvania is almost a
consumer tip:
  Who was fatally burned
  March 21, 1870
  by the explosion of a lamp
  filled with "R.E. Danforth's
  Non-Explosive Burning Fluid"

Oops! Harry Edsel Smith of Albany, New York:
  Born 1903--Died 1942
  Looked up the elevator shaft to see if
  the car was on the way down. It was.

In a Thurmont, Maryland, cemetery:
  Here lies an Atheist
  All dressed up
  And no place to go.

But does he make house calls? Dr. Fred Roberts, Brookland, Arkansas:
  Office upstairs

2. A tourist in Vienna is going through a graveyard and all of a
sudden he hears some music. No one is around, so he starts search-

ing for the source. He finally locates the origin and finds it is coming from a grave with a headstone that reads: Ludwig van Beethoven, 1770-1827.

Then he realizes that the music is the Ninth Symphony and it is being played backward! Puzzled, he leaves the graveyard and persuades a friend to return with him. By the time they arrive back at the grave, the music has changed. This time it is the Seventh Symphony, but like the previous piece, it is being played backward. Curious, the men agree to consult a music scholar.

When they return with the expert, the Fifth Symphony is playing, again backward. The expert notices that the symphonies are being played in the reverse order in which they were composed, the 9th, then the 7th, then the 5th.

By the next day the word has spread and a throng has gathered around the grave. They are all listening to the Second Symphony being played backward.

Just then the graveyard's caretaker ambles up to the group. Someone in the group asks him if he has an explanation for the music.

"Don't you get it?" the caretaker says incredulously.

"He's decomposing."

Women's Jokes

1. THE TRUTH ABOUT EVE
One day in the Garden of Eden, Eve calls out to God, "Lord, I have a problem!"
"What's the problem, Eve?"
"Lord, I know you've created me and have provided this beautiful garden and all of these wonderful animals, and that hilarious comedy snake, but I'm just not happy. "
Why is that, Eve?" came the reply from above.
"Lord, I am lonely. And I'm sick to death of apples."
"Well, Eve, in that case I have a solution. I shall create a man for you." "What's a 'man,' Lord?"
"This man will be a flawed creature, with aggressive tendencies, an enormous ego and an inability to empathize or listen to you properly. All in all he'll give you a hard time. But he'll be bigger and faster and more muscular than you, he'll be really good at fighting and kicking a ball about and hunting fleet-footed ruminants, and not altogether bad in the sack."
"Sounds great," says Eve, with an ironically raised eyebrow.
"Yeah, well. He's better than a poke in the eye with a burnt stick, but you can have him only on one condition. "
What's that, Lord?"
"You'll have to let him believe that I made him first."

2. Several years ago I bought a beautiful green beaded gown to wear when I was going to be the Emcee for the Oklahoma Maid of Cotton. Then a few weeks later I attended a funeral in my home town. My sister-in-law, two of my daughters and I had ridden together to the cemetery and then went passed my grandparents graves. I stated, "Now remember girls, when I die, I am suppose to be buried here by my grandparents. And also, remember that I want the least expensive casket possible, and only one long stem red rose on it. Do NOT spend a lot of money on my funeral. The only thing I want you to promise is that you have me looking as nice as possible. In fact, I look pretty good in that green beaded

dress." My daughter, Cari said, "So would I, Mother, so would I and believe me. You ARE NOT going to be buried in that dress!"

3. Subject: Random Thoughts
Growing old is mandatory; growing up is optional.
Insanity is my only means of relaxation.
Forget the health food. I need all the preservatives I can get.
Blessed are those who hunger and thirst, for they are sticking to their diets.
You're getting old when you get the same sensation from a rocking chair that you once got from a roller coaster.
Perhaps you know why women over fifty don't have babies: They would put them down somewhere and forget where they left them.
My mind not only wanders, sometimes it leaves completely.
Every time I think about exercise, I lie down til the thought goes away.
God put me on earth to accomplish a certain number of things. Right now I am so far behind, I will live forever.
It's frustrating when you know all the answers, but nobody bothers to ask you the questions. If you can remain calm, you just don't have all the facts.
Stress reducer: Put a bag on your head. Mark it "Closed for remodeling." **caution - leave air holes.
I finally got my head together, and my body fell apart.
There cannot be a crisis this week; my schedule is already full.
The real art of conversation is not only to say the right thing in the right place, but also to leave unsaid the wrong thing at the tempting moment.
The best way to forget all your troubles is to wear tight shoes.
The nice part of living in a small town is that when I don't know what I'm doing, someone else does.
The older you get, the tougher it is to lose weight, because by then your body and your fat are really good friends.
Age doesn't always bring wisdom. Sometimes age comes alone.
Just when I was getting used to yesterday, along came today.
Sometimes I think I understand everything, then I regain conscious-

ness.

You don't stop laughing because you grow old; you grow old because you stop laughing.

I don't mind the rat race, but I could do with a little more cheese.

I had to give up jogging for my health. My thighs kept rubbing together and setting my pantyhose on fire.

Amazing! You just hang something in your closet for a while, and it shrinks two sizes.

Age is important only if you're a cheese.

Freedom of the press means no-iron clothes.

Inside some of us is a thin person struggling to get out, but she can usually be sedated with a few pieces of chocolate cake.

Seen it all, done it all, can't remember most of it.

4. The New Over 40 Barbie Doll

1. Bifocals Barbie. Comes with her own set of blended-lens fashion frames in six wild colors (half-frames too!), neck chain and large-print editions of Vogue and Martha Stewart Living.

2. Hot Flash Barbie. Press Barbie's belly button and watch her face turn beet red while tiny drops of perspiration appear on her forehead! With hand held fan and tiny tissues.

3. Facial Hair Barbie. As Barbie's hormone levels shift, see her whisker grow! Available with teensy tweezers and magnifying mirror.

4. Cook's Arms Barbie. Hide Barbie's droopy triceps with these new, roomier-sleeved gowns. Good news on the tummy front, too: muumuus are back! Cellulite cream and loofah sponge optional.

5. Bunion Barbie. Years of disco dancing in stiletto heels have definitely taken their toll on Barbie's dainty arched feet. Soothe her sores with this pumice stone and plasters, then slip on soft terry mules. Colors: pink, rose, blush.

6. No More Wrinkles Barbie. Erase those pesky crow's-feet and lip lines with a tube of Skin Sparkle-Spackle, from Barbie's own line of exclusive age-blasting cosmetics.

7. Soccer Mom Barbie. All that experience as a cheerleader is really paying off as Barbie dusts off her old high school megaphone

to root for Babs and Ken Jr. With minivan in robin egg blue or white, and cooler filled with doughnut holes and fruit punch.

8. Mid-life Crisis Barbie. It's time to ditch Ken. Barbie needs a change, and Bruce (her personal trainer) is just what the doctor ordered along with Prozac. They're hopping in her new red Miata and heading for the Napa Valley to open a B&B. Comes with real tape of "Breaking Up Is Hard to Do."

9. Single Mother Barbie. There's not much time for primping anymore! Ken's shacked up with the Swedish au pair in the Dream House and Barbie's across town with Babs and Ken Jr. in a fourth-floor walk-up. Barbie's selling off her old gowns and accessories to raise rent money. Complete garage sale kit included.

10. Recovery Barbie. Too many parties have finally caught up with the ultimate party girl. Now she does 12 steps instead of dance steps! Clean and sober, she's going to meetings religiously. Comes with little copy of The Big Book and six-pack of Diet Coke.

11. Nursing Home Barbie. Who knows when Barbie will have outlived her usefulness? From Dream House to Nursing Home (both new and improved wheelchair-accessible and retrofitted to conform to ADA code requirements), the possibilities (not to mention the accessories) are endless.

12. Over 40 Rich-Tone Barbie. Comes complete with three gold medals, an extra large day-timer, sequins, orthopedic boots and crutches for those missed choreography steps, and a special hearing aid for those hard to hear chords. Prozac available for those pre-contest days.

5. Subject: Pick-Up line responses

Attention female readers! Are you sick and tired of those stupid old pick-up lines that men continue to use? Here are some great comebacks!

Man: "Haven't we met before?"
Woman: "Perhaps. I'm the receptionist at the VD Clinic."
Man: "Haven't I seen you someplace before?
Woman: "Yeah, that's why I don't go there anymore."
Man: "Is this seat empty?"

Woman: "Yes, and this one will be too if you sit down."
Man: "So, wanna go back to my place?"
Woman: "Well, I don't know. Will two people fit under a rock?"
Man: "Your place or mine?"
Woman: "Both. You go to yours and I'll go to mine."
Man: "I'd like to call you. What's your number?"
Woman: "It's in the phone book."
Man: "But I don't know your name."
Woman: "That's in the phone book too."
Man: "So what do you do for a living?"
Woman: "I'm a female impersonator."
Man: "Hey, baby, what's your sign?"
Woman: "Do not enter"
Man: "How do you like your eggs in the morning?"
Woman: "Unfertilized!"
Man: "Hey, come on, we're both here at this bar for the same reason"
Woman: "Yeah! Let's pick up some chicks!"
Man: "I know how to please a woman."
Woman: "Then please leave me alone."
Man: "I want to give myself to you."
Woman: "Sorry, I don't accept cheap gifts."
Man: "If I could see you naked, I'd die happy:
Woman: "Yeah, but if I saw you naked, I'd probably die laughing".
Man: "Your body is like a temple."
Woman: "Sorry, there are no services today."
Man: "I'd go through anything for you."
Woman: "Good! Let's start with your bank account."
Man: "I would go to the end of the world for you.
Woman: "Yes, but would you stay there?

6.   Veteran Pillsbury spokes-model Pop N. Fresh died yesterday of a severe yeast infection. He was 71. Fresh was buried in one of the largest funeral ceremonies in recent years. Dozens of celebrities turned out including Mrs. Butterworth, the California Raisins, Hungry Jack, Betty Crocker, Chef Boyardee, and the Hostess Twinkies. The gravesite was piled high with flours as longtime friend Aunt

Jemima delivered the eulogy, describing Fresh as a man who never knew how much he was kneaded. Fresh rose quickly in show business, but his later life was filled with many turnovers. He was not considered a very smart cookie, wasting much of his dough on half-baked schemes. Still, even as a crusty old man, he was a roll model for millions.

Fresh is survived by his second wife. They have two children and another in the oven. The funeral was held at 3:50 for about 20 minutes.

7. I'M A SENIOR CITIZEN
* I'm the life of the party...even when it lasts 'till 8 pm.
* I'm very good at opening childproof caps with a hammer.
* I'm usually interested in going home before I get to where I'm going.
* I'm good on a trip for at least an hour without my aspirin, antacid...
* I'm the first one to find the bathroom wherever I go
* I'm awake many hours before my body allows me to get up
* I'm smiling all the time because I can't hear a word you're saying
* I'm very good at telling stories...over and over and over and over
* I'm aware that other people's grandchildren are not as bright as mine are
* I'm so cared for: long-term care, eye care, private care, and dental care
* I'm not grouchy, I just don't like traffic, waiting, children, politicians...
* I'm positive I did housework correctly before the Internet
* I'm sure everything I can't find is in a secure place
* I'm wrinkled, saggy and lumpy, and that's just my left leg
* I'm having trouble remembering simple words like.... Uh....
* I'm now spending more time with my pillows than with my mate realizing that aging is not for sissies
* I'm walking more (to the bathroom) and enjoying it less
* I'm going to reveal what goes on behind the green doors...
* I'm sure they are making adults much younger these days

* I'm in the *initial* state of my golden years: SS, CD's, IRA's, and AARP
* I'm wondering if you're only as old as you feel, how could I be alive at 150?
* I'm anti-everything now: anti-fat, anti-smoke, anti-noise, anti-inflammatory
* I'm supporting all movements now...by eating bran, prunes and raisins
* I'm a walking storeroom of facts...I've just lost the storeroom
* I'm a Senior Citizen and I think I am having the time of my life
* Do I have Alzheimers? I don't remember. But, I'm happy, I think.

8. Could this be men instead of cats?
1. Cats do what they want, when they want.
2. They rarely listen to you.
3. They're totally unpredictable.
4. They whine when they are not happy.
5. When you want to play they want to be left alone.
6. When you want to be alone, they want to play.
7. They expect you to cater to their every whim.
8. They're moody.
9. They leave their hair everywhere.
10. They drive you nuts.
Conclusion: Cats are little, tiny women in cheap fur coats.

9. THE TWELVE THANK-YOU NOTES OF CHRISTMAS
My dearest darling Edward,   Dec. 25
What a wonderful surprise has just greeted me! That sweet partridge, in that lovely little pear-tree; what an enchanting, romantic, poetic present! Bless you, and thank you.
Your deeply loving
Emily

Beloved Edward,   Dec. 26
The two turtle-doves arrived this morning, and are cooing away in the pear-tree as I write. I'm so touched and grateful!

With undying love, as always,
Emily

My darling Edward,   Dec. 27
You do think of the most original presents! Who ever thought of sending anybody three French hens? Do they really come all the way from France? It's a pity we have no chicken coops, but I expect we'll find some. Anyway, thank you so much; they're lovely
Your devoted Emily

Dearest Edward,   Dec. 28
What a surprise! Four calling birds arrived this morning. They are very sweet, even if they do call rather loudly--they make telephoning almost impossible--but I expect they'll calm down when they get used to their new home. Anyway, I'm very grateful, of course I am.
 Love from Emily

Dearest Edward,
    Dec. 29

The mailman has just delivered five most beautiful gold rings one for each finger, and all fitting perfectly! A really lovely present! Lovelier, in a way, than birds, which do take rather a lot of looking after. The four that arrived yesterday are still making a terrible row, and I'm afraid none of us got much sleep last night. Mother says she wants to use the rings to "wring" their necks. Mother has such a sense of humor. This time she's only joking, I think, but I do know what she means. Still, I love the rings.
Bless you,

Emily
Dear Edward,   Dec. 30

Whatever I expected to find when I opened the front door this morning, it certainly wasn't six great geese laying eggs all over the

porch. Frankly, I rather hoped that you had stopped sending me birds. We have no room for them, and they've already ruined the croquet lawn. I know you meant well, but let's call a halt, shall we?
Love,
Emily

Edward,   Dec. 31
I thought I said NO MORE BIRDS. This morning I woke up to find no more than seven swans, all trying to get into our tiny goldfish pond. I'd rather not think what's happened to the goldfish. The whole house seems to be full of birds, to say nothing of what they leave behind them, so please, please, stop!
Your Emily

Jan 1
Frankly, I prefer the birds. What am I to do with eight milkmaids? And their cows! Is this some kind of a joke? If so, I'm afraid I don't find it very amusing.
Emily

Look here, Edward,   Jan 2

This has gone far enough. You say you're sending me nine ladies dancing. All I can say is, judging from the way they dance; they're certainly not ladies. The village just isn't accustomed to seeing a regiment of shameless viragos, with nothing on but their lipstick, cavorting round the green, and it's Mother and I who get the blame.
If you value our friendship, which I do (less and less), kindly stop this ridiculous behavior at once!
Emily

Jan 3
As I write this letter, ten disgusting old men are prancing up and down all over what used to be the garden, before the geese and the swans and the cows got at it. And several of them, I have just noticed, are taking inexcusable liberties with the milkmaids. Mean-

while the neighbors are trying to have us evicted. I shall never speak to you again.
Emily

Jan 4

This is the last straw! You know I detest bagpipes! The place has now become something between a menagerie and a madhouse, and a man from the council has just declared it unfit for habitation. At least Mother has been spared this last outrage; they took her away yesterday afternoon in an ambulance. I hope you're satisfied.

Sir,   Jan 5

Our client, Miss Emily Wilbraham, instructs me to inform you that with the arrival on her premises at 7:30 this morning of the entire percussion section of the Boston Symphony Orchestra, and several of their friends, she has no course left open to her but to seek an injunction to prevent you importuning her further. I am making arrangements for the return of much assorted livestock.

I am, Sir,
yours faithfully,
G. Creep
Attorney at law

10. Titles of the 25 Shortest Book   (You might never see in print)
25. MY PLAN TO FIND THE REAL KILLERS-by O J Simpson
24. THE ENGINEER'S GUIDE TO FASHION
23. TO ALL THE MEN I'VE LOVED BEFORE-by Ellen De-Generes
22. THE DIFFERENCE BETWEEN REALITY AND DILBERT
21. HUMAN RIGHTS ADVANCES IN CHINA
20. THINGS I WOULD NOT DO FOR MONEY-by Dennis Rod-man
19. THE WILD YEARS-by Al Gore
18. AMELIA EARHART'S GUIDE TO THE PACIFIC OCEAN

17. AMERICA'S MOST POPULAR LAWYERS
16. CAREER OPPORTUNITIES FOR LIBERAL ARTS
MAJORS
15. DETROIT - A TRAVEL GUIDE
14. DIFFERENT WAYS TO SPELL BOB
13. DR. KEVORKIAN'S COLLECTION OF
MOTIVATIONAL SPEECHES
12. EASY UNIX
11. ETHIOPIAN TIPS ON WORLD DOMINANCE
10. EVERYTHING MEN KNOW ABOUT WOMEN
9. EVERYTHING WOMEN KNOW ABOUT MEN
8. FRENCH HOSPITALITY
7. GEORGE FOREMAN'S BIG BOOK OF BABY NAMES
6. HOW TO SUSTAIN A MUSICAL CAREER-by Art Garfunkel
5. MIKE TYSON'S GUIDE TO DATING ETIQUETTE
4. SPOTTED OWL RECIPES-by the EPA
3. STAPLE YOUR WAY TO SUCCESS
2. THE AMISH PHONE DIRECTORY
And the Number one World's Shortest book:
1. THE BOOK OF VIRTUES-by Bill Clinton

12. An Irishman named Murphy went to his doctor after a long illness. The doctor, after a lengthy examination, sighed and looked Murphy in the eye and said, "I've some bad news for you ... you have the cancer and it can't be cured. I'd give you two weeks to a month." Murphy, shocked and saddened by the news, but of solid character, managed to compose himself and walk from the doctor's office into the waiting room. There he saw his son who had been waiting. Murphy said, "Son, we Irish celebrate when things are good and celebrate when things don't go so well. In this case, things aren't so well. I have cancer and I've been given a short time to live. Let's head for the pub and have a few pints."

After three or four pints the two were feeling a little less somber. There were some laughs and more beers. They were eventually approached by some of Murphy's old friends who asked what the two were celebrating. Murphy told them that the Irish celebrate the good and the bad. He went on to tell them that they were drinking to his impending end. He told his friends "I've only got a few weeks to live as I have been diagnosed with AIDS."

The friends gave Murphy their condolences and they had a couple more beers. After his friends left, Murphy's son leaned over and whispered his confusion.

"Dad I thought you said that you were dying from cancer...? You just told your friends that you were dying from AIDS?"

Murphy said, "I am dying from cancer son, I just don't want any of them sleeping with your mother after I'm gone."

14. On Growing Older

A man has reached middle age when he is cautioned to slow down by his doctor instead of by the police.

Middle age is having a choice of two temptations and choosing the one that will get you home earlier.

You know you're into middle age when you realize that caution is the only thing you care to exercise.

My grandmother's 90; she's dating a man 93. They never argue: they can't hear each other.

At my age, "getting a little action" means I don't need to take a laxative.

I have my 87th birthday coming up, and people ask me what I'd most appreciate getting. I tell them: a paternity suit.

As I grow older and older, And totter toward the tomb, I find that I care less and less, Who goes to bed with whom.

Don't worry about avoiding temptation. As you grow older, it will avoid you.

Be nice to your children, for they will choose your rest home.

Life is never fair, and perhaps it is a good thing for most of us that it is not.

Don't take life so seriously ... it's not permanent.

Despite the cost of living, it's still quite popular.

The trouble with life is, by the time you can read a girl like a book, your library card has expired.

Experience teaches you to recognize a mistake when you've made it again.

If you're old enough to know better, you're too old to do it.

The aging process could be slowed down if it had to work its way through Congress.

I have everything I had 20 years ago, only it's all a little bit lower.

Time wounds all heels.

You're getting old when getting lucky means you find your car in the parking lot.

You're getting old when you're sitting in a rocker and you can't get it started.

You're getting old when tying one on means fastening your Medic Alert bracelet.

You're getting old when your wife gives up sex for Lent, and you don't know till the 4th of July.

You're getting old when you don't care where your wife goes, just so you don't have to go along.

You're getting old when you wake up with that morning-after feeling, and you didn't do anything the night before.

I'm getting just like my great-grandchildren -- wearing diapers and using a walker.

The cardiologist's diet: if it tastes good, spit it out.

Doctor to patient: I have good news and bad news: the good news is that you are not a hypochondriac.

It's hard to be nostalgic when you can't remember anything.

You know you're getting old when you stop buying green bananas.

Death is not the end; there remains the litigation over the estate.

My uncle reads the obits every day. He can't understand how people always die in alphabetical order.

Last Will and Testament: Being of sound mind, I spent all my money.

15. A mother and her small daughter were in New York City. The mother was trying to hail a cab, when her daughter noticed several wildly dressed women who were loitering on a nearby street corner. The mother finally hailed her cab and they both climbed in, at which point the daughter asks her mother, "Mommy, what are all

those ladies waiting for by that corner?" "Those ladies are waiting for their husbands to come home from work," replied the mother. The cabbie, upon hearing this exchange, turns to the mother and says, "Ah, C'mon lady! Tell your daughter the truth! For crying out loud, they're hookers!" The mother became quite annoyed with the cabbie for being so blunt. A brief period of silence followed, and the daughter then asked, "Mommy, do the ladies have any children?" "Of course, dear. Where do you think cabbies come from?"

17. A hurricane came unexpectedly. The ship went down and was lost. The man found himself swept up on the shore of an island with no other people, no supplies, nothing. Only bananas and coconuts. Used to 5-star hotels, this guy had no idea what to do, so for the next four months he ate bananas, drank coconut juice, longed for his old life and fixed his gaze on the sea, hoping to spot a rescue ship.

One day, as he was lying on the beach, he spotted movement out of the corner of his eye. It was a rowboat, and in it was the most gorgeous woman he had ever seen. She rowed up to him. In disbelief, he asked her: "Where did you come from? How did you get here?"

"I rowed from the other side of the island," she said. "I landed here when my cruise ship sank." "Amazing," he said. "I didn't know anyone else had survived. How many are there? You were lucky to have a rowboat wash up with you."

"It's only me," she said, "and the rowboat didn't wash up; nothing did." He was confused. "Then how did you get the rowboat?"

"Oh, simple," replied the woman. "I made the rowboat out of materials that I found on the island. The oars were whittled from Gum tree branches. I wove the bottom from palm branches and the sides and stern came from a Eucalyptus tree."

"B-B-But that's impossible," stuttered the man. "You had no tools or hardware. How did you manage?"

"Oh, that was no problem," replied the woman. "On the other side of the island there is a very unusual stratum of alluvial rock exposed I found that if I fired it to a certain temperature in my kiln, it melted into forgeable ductile iron. I used that for tools, and used the tools to make the hardware. But enough of that," she said. "Where do you live?"

Sheepishly, he confessed that he had been sleeping on the beach the whole time.

"Well, let's row over to my place, then," she said.

After a few minutes of rowing she docked the boat at a small wharf. As the man looked to the shore he nearly fell out of the boat. Before him was a stone walk leading to an exquisite bungalow painted in blue and white. While the woman tied up the rowboat with an expertly woven hemp rope, the man could only stare ahead, dumb struck. As they walked into the house, she said casually, "It's not much, but I call it home. Sit down, please; would you like a drink?"

"No, no thank you," he said, still dazed. "I can't take any more coconut juice."

"It's not coconut juice," the woman replied. "I have a still. How about a Pina Colada?" Trying to hide his amazement, the man accepted, and they sat down on her couch to talk.

After they had exchanged their stories, the woman announced, "I'm going to slip into something comfortable. Would you like to take a shower and shave? There is a razor upstairs in the cabinet in the bathroom."

No longer questioning anything, the man went into the bathroom. There in the cabinet was a razor made from a bone handle. Two shells honed to a hollow ground edge were fastened onto its end inside a swivel mechanism.

"This woman is amazing," he mused. "What next?"

When he returned, she greeted him wearing nothing but vines - strategically positioned - and smelling faintly of gardenias. She beckoned for him to sit down next to her. "Tell me," she began, suggestively, slithering closer to him, "we've been out here for a very long time. You've been lonely. There's something I'm sure you really feel like doing right now, something you've been longing for all these months. You know..." She stared into his eyes.

He couldn't believe what he was hearing.

"You mean--" he replied "I can check my e-mail from here?"

18. The young man asked his neighbor how to make certain to be the boss in the house. "Why every so often I tell my wife that I am the boss and that is that!" The next evening the young man told his wife that he was the boss and that was that! She looked at him and asked, "How would you like not to see me for a few days?" Well he didn't see her at all the first day. Didn't see her on the second day. On the third day he could see just a little bit of her out of one eye.

19. I have become quite a frivolous old gal. I'm seeing five gentlemen everyday. As soon as I awake, Will Power helps me out of bed. When he leaves I go see John. Then Charley Horse comes along. When he is here, he takes a lot of my attention. When he leaves, Arthur Ritis shows up and stays the rest of the day. He doesn't like to stay in one place very long so he takes me from joint to joint. After such a busy day, I'm really tired and ready to go to bed with Ben Gay. What a day!

20. An older woman ordered a double scotch with 2 drops of water. The bartender was puzzled about the drops of water but served it anyway. Finishing it, she ordered another made the very same way. This time he just had to question her about the two drops of water. She replied, "Mister you sure don't know anything about us senior citizens. We can hold our scotch. We just can't hold our water!"

21. A woman was determined to break her new foul-mouthed parrot from cursing. The first time the parrot let out a sentence of obscenities, the woman stuck the parrot in the freezer. Five minutes later when retrieving the bird he pleaded, "Lady, I'll not curse again. Please don't stick me in that freezer." Months went by and the parrot got excited and shouted out another obscene sentence. Again the woman shoved the bird in the freezer. Ten minutes later when retrieved, the parrot again promised not to curse again. Everything was going fine until one day in November the parrot got scared and cursed another sentence. This time the woman stuck

him in the freezer, intending to leave him 15 minutes but the phone rang. Thirty minute passed before she remembered the parrot. She retrieved the bird; began brushing the ice from his wings. His beak and his feathers. The parrot finally began to thaw. He asked, "Just one question lady. What on earth was said by that turkey in there?"

22. Employee memo Bathroom Policy

In the past, employees were permitted to make trips to the restroom under informal guidelines. Effective September 1, a restroom trip policy will be established to provide a more consistent method of accounting for each employee's restroom time and ensuring equal treatment of all employees.

Under the policy a "restroom trip bank" will be established for each employee. The first day of each month, employees will be given twenty restroom trip credits. These credits may be accumulated. Within two weeks, the entrance doors to all restrooms are being equipped with personal identification stations and computer-linked voice print recognition devices. Before the end of September, each employee must provide two copies of voice prints (one normal and one under stress) to the human resources department. The voice print recognition stations will be operational but not restrictive for the month of September. Employees should acquaint themselves with the stations during that period.

If the employee's restroom trip bank balances reaches zero, the doors to the restroom will not unlock for that employee's voice until the first of the next month. In addition, all restroom stalls are being equipped with timed paper roll retractors. If the stall is occupied for more than three minutes, an alarm will sound. Thirty seconds after the alarm sounds, the roll of paper will retract into the wall, the toilet will flush, and the stall door will open. If the stall remains occupied, your picture will be taken. The picture will then be posted on the bulletin board. Anyone's picture showing up three times will immediately be terminated. If you have any questions about this policy, please ask your supervisor. They have received advance instructions.

23. IF YOU GOTTA GO, START EARLY

My friend is a rather old-fashioned lady, always quite delicate and elegant, especially in her language. She and her husband were planning a week's vacation in Florida, so she wrote to a particular campground and asked for a reservation. She wanted to make sure the campground was fully equipped, but didn't quite know how to ask about the toilet facilities. She just couldn't bring herself to write the word "toilet" in her letter. After much deliberation, she finally came up with the old-fashioned term "bathroom commode." But, when she wrote that down, she still thought she was being too forward. So, she started all over again, rewrote the entire letter, and referred to the bathroom commode merely as the B.C. "Does the campground have it's own B.C." is what she wrote.

Well, the campground owner wasn't old-fashioned at all, and when he got the letter, he just couldn't figure out what the woman was talking about. That B.C. business really stumped him. After worrying about it for a while, he showed the letter to several campers, but they couldn't imagine what the lady meant either. So, the campground owner, finally coming to the conclusion that the lady must be asking the about the location of the local Baptist Church, sat down and wrote the following reply:

Dear Madam: I regret very much the delay in answering your letter, but I now take the pleasure of informing you that a B.C. is located nine miles north of the campground and is capable of seating 250 people at one time. I admit it is quite a distance away if you are in the habit of going regularly, but no doubt you will be please to know that a great number of people take their lunches along and make a day of it. They usually arrive early and stay late. The last time my wife and I went was six years ago, and it was so crowded that we had to stand up the whole time we were there. It may interest you to know that now there is a supper planned to raise money to buy more seats. They are going to hold it in the basement of the B.C. I would like to say it pains me very much not to be able to go more regularly, but it surely is no lack of desire on my part. As we grow older, it seems to be more an effort, particularly in cold weather. If you do decide to come down to our campground, perhaps I could go with you the first time you go, sit with you, and introduce you to all the other folks. Remember, this IS a friendly community."

24. This lonely single woman was always being advised that she wouldn't be lonely if she just bought herself a pet. (I have butterflies on the wall and a pillow in shape of a duck, and that is all I need.) Finally, this lonely single woman went to a pet store and right by the front door was frog in a cage. When she looked at it, it went, "Smack, Smack!" She though, "Wow a kissing frog." She looked all over the pet store, viewing darling purring kittens and cuddly puppies wagging their tails at her. There was a Myna bird that whistled and said, "Hi, Babe!" She thought, "now that might be nice to come home to every day." Between looking at these animals and birds she kept stealing glances at the frog. Every time the frog would "smack" a kiss at her. Finally, she purchased the frog. She was driving home with the frog in a box with the seat belt around it. While waiting at a stop light she took the lid off the box. Once again the frog went, "Smack." She picked up the frog and kissed it. Immediately, it turned into the most gorgeous hunk of man she ever saw in her life. But do you know what she turned into? The first motel she found! Since then I have checked out every pet store everywhere I go and it doesn't work!

25. Some marriages are doomed for divorce, especially when the groom is still tied to his Mother's apron. The bride may have to send him back to Mother. She should attached this note. "I've tried, but just can't compete with how wonderful your cooking always is." Sincerely, Would-be-wife. PS He'll eat anything as long as it's cooked exactly the way you always cooked it, just like he likes it!

26. When one woman was being introduced to another she said, "You look just like Helen Brown." "Well," the other woman snorted, "You don't look so hot in blue either!"

27. Men may say that women talk way too much. They don't complain all when the women are telling the men how wonderful they are!

28. Seen on a bumper sticker, "I still miss my ex---but my aim is getting better all the time!"

29. The doctor shook his head at the 62 year old woman. He stated "I can't believe it. You are pregnant!' She exclaimed, "I can't be. I'm 62 years old and my husband is 75." The doctor said he knew all this and was surprised too. Then he asked, "How is your husband going to take this?" The woman decided to call him right then and there. When he answered she shouted, "You old coot, you got me pregnant!" After a long pause, he asked, "Who is this?"

30. An eighty year old woman made the comment that she became irritated when people say, "have a nice day" without meaning it. When young men say it she asks, "What did you have in mind?"

31. At a meeting discussing the American Disabilities Act, someone told about a man named Chris. He had a sex operation and became a woman named Chris. Upon returning to work, no one would work with Chris so the management had to fire him. The question, "Was it covered under ADA or Workmen's Compensation?" After a lengthy discussion, one woman stated, "At least now, Chris doesn't have a disability any more!"

32. There once was an old maid from Duluth,
Who cried when she thought of her youth.
She thought of the chances,
 she missed at school dances.
And once in a telephone booth!

33. Do you know what you call a man who has lost 90% of his thinking power? A widower!

34. Three men were walking along a beach and found an old bottle. One of them began rubbing the bottle and out popped a Genie. The Genie was so grateful for escaping the bottle that he granted each of them a wish. The first man wished that he was 10 times smarter than he was and instantly he was. The second man stated that he wished that he was 50 times smarter. Instantly he was! The third man stated that he wished he was 100 times smarter. The Genie questioned him asking, "Are you sure?" The man said he was sure certain that he was sure. "100 times smarter is what I want!' And instantly he was changed into a woman!

35. Someone once asked me what I would do when I stopped working. I said that with five children I could divide the year up and spend 10 weeks, 3 days and 4 hours with each one of them. One of my children said that would be fine for the first year but then what was I going to do?

36. Remember, we old folks are worth a fortune. We have silver in our hair, gold in our teeth, stones in our kidneys, lead in our feet, and gas in our stomachs.

37. This is a child's view of a retirement in a mobile home park. After a Christmas break, the teacher asked her small pupils how they spent their holiday. One small boy's reply went like this:
We always spend Christmas with Grandpa and Grandma. They used to live in a big brick house. But Grandpa got retreaded and they moved to Texas. They live in a place with lot of retreaded people. They live in tin huts. They ride three-wheel tricycles. They go to a big building they call a wrecked hall. But if it is a wrecked hall, it is fixed now. They play games there and do exercises, but they don't do them too good. There is a swimming pool and they go to it and just stand there in the water with their hats on. I guess they don't know how to swim. My Grandma used to bake cookies and stuff, but I guess she forgot how. Nobody cooks, - they

all go to restaurants.

As you come into the park there is a doll house with a man sitting in it. He watches all day, so they can't get out without him seeing them. They wear badges with their names on them. I guess they don't know who they are anymore. My Grandma says Grandpa worked hard all his life and earned his retreadment. I wish they would move back home. But I guess the man in the doll house won't let them out.

38. I am always being a told "old women" joke and I'm not sure of the reason.

A young man was driving across the panhandle of Oklahoma during a blinding snowstorm and finally got stuck in a drift. After he made his way to a house nearby, he asked the little old widow woman if he could possibly spend the night. Now, this woman looked on him with compassion, pity, and LUST! She asked him to remain in the foyer while she went into the other room for a minute. When she returned she had her hands cupped together. She said, "Sonny, you may spend the night here. And if you can guess what's in my hands you can sleep with me!" The young man was sharp and knew another meaning of the word "sleep with." He was even thinking he might rather freeze in the car than "sleep with her." After careful consideration he guessed that she must be holding an elephant in her hands. Her reply, "Close enough!"

39. Subject: How to set a table

Just keep this in mind when preparing or helping to prepare that special day. Happy Thanksgiving!

This is more embarrassing for my mother than for me because I wasn't quite 4 years old when it happened. My mother taught me to read when I was 3 years old (her first mistake). One day I was in the bathroom and noticed one of the cabinet door was ajar. I read the box in the cabinet. I then asked my mother why she was keeping napkins in the bathroom. Didn't they belong in the kitchen? Not wanting to burden me with unnecessary facts she told me that those were for special occasions.

Now fast forward a few months. It's Thanksgiving Day and my folks are leaving to pick up the pastor and his wife for dinner. Mom had assignments for all of us while they were gone. Mine was to set the table. You guessed it! When they returned, the pastor came in first and immediately burst into laughter. Next came his wife who gasped, then began giggling. Next came my father, who roared with laughter. Then came mom, who almost died of embarrassment when she saw each place setting on the table with a "special occasion" napkin at each plate, with the fork carefully arranged on top. I had even tucked the little tails in so they didn't hang off the edge. My mother asked me why I used these and of course my response sent the other adults into further fits of laughter. "But Mom, you SAID they were for special occasions!!"

Author unknown or wouldn't admit to it.!!!

40.   Two traveling salesmen, Tom and Andy, were driving through the hot desert. They stopped at a farmhouse and asked the little old widow woman if they could spend the night. Nine months and 3 days later Tom called Andy. He asked, "Do you remember that night when we stayed all night at the widow woman's house?" Andy replied, "Yeah." Tom asked, "Well, did you wander down the hall during the night into the old woman's room?" Andy replied, "Yeah." Tom asked, "Did you make passionate love to her?" Andy replied, "Yeah." Tom asked, "Did you use my name instead of yours?" Andy again replied, "Yeah." Tom stated, "Well, thanks a lot, buddy. She just died and left me a fortune!"

41.   I don't know how many of you might be single again. In case you aren't, you surely know someone who is in that group. Dating for the "Single Again" is a joke. (I am sure that this works with both sexes.) I have dated some of those jokes. I seem to attract the guys who say, "Why honey, you can trust me. Why the last thing I would want to do is hurt you." They were telling the truth: it was the last thing. There were just a whole bunch of other things they wanted to do first!

42.   I heard of a club I could have joined. It was the USWTI-SOMWANGMOHUOTM. Stands for "United Single Women Together In Search Of Men Who Are Not Gay, Married, Or Hung Up On Their Mothers."

43.   Several years ago, when my former husband was between wives someone asked me what my children would think if we remarried. I said that was not a chance. Nevertheless, they were curious about what my children would think. A few weeks later when the children were all at home I proposed the question. My oldest son, Tony, said, "Well, Mom, we would buy you an entire new wardrobe." Got my attention immediately so I asked, "Why?" He continued, "All straight jackets!" Case closed.

44.   My former husband has had a few other wives since me. At different times some of my children have been close friends with their stepmothers (or my step-wives). Usually no two of them like the same woman at the same time. One day at my house, my two oldest daughters, Shari & Cari were arguing about two of the ex-wives. Both of the ex-wives were involved with the former husband. Shari stated that she thought Cari was being too darn friendly with wife #3. Cari retaliated with, "Me, what about you, you are so chummy-chummy with wife #2." My youngest daughter, Kristi, spoke up then and said, "It's a wonder either one of you have anything to do with me. I am crazy about wife #1."

45. Three women who lived in the same apartment building were having all sorts of troubles. As hard as they tried, no one would give in to the demands of the others. Each woman hired an attorney, and each attorney worked diligently to settle the disputes outside of court. But no amount of entreaty or compromise worked. Each woman dug her foot deeper in her "sand" and refused to budge. Finally, the day came when all three were in court. The judge, with Solomon-like-wisdom, decreed, "I'll hear the oldest first." The case was closed.

46. Recently, when donating blood, one of the volunteers cautioned us not to do any heavy work like cooking or cleaning. I told her that I don't believe in using, or doing, four letter words like cook, bake, wash, iron, dust, or diet! She thought that was one of the funniest remarks she had ever heard. Every few minutes she would come over to ask me what they were since she kept omitting one of them. In fact, I have a T-shirt with that on the back. The order blank is in the back of the book.

47. A young 23 old woman, Linda, was visiting her in-laws. While there, she went to a nearby supermarket to pick up some groceries. Several people noticed her sitting in her car with the windows rolled up, her eyes closed, and both hands behind the back of her head. One customer who had been at the store for a while became concerned and walked over to the car. He noticed that Linda's eyes were now open, and she looked very strange. He asked her if she was okay, and Linda replied that she'd been shot in the back of the head, and had been holding her brains in for over an hour. The man called the paramedics, who broke into the car because the doors were locked, and Linda refused to remove her hands from her head.

When they finally got in, they found that Linda had a wad of bread dough on the back of her head. A Pillsbury biscuit canister had exploded from the heat, making a loud noise that sounded like a gunshot, and the wad of dough hit her in the back of her head. When she reached back to find out what it was, she felt the dough and thought it was her brains.

She had initially passed out, but quickly recovered and tried to hold her brains in for over an hour-until someone noticed and came to her aid. And, yes, she is a blonde.

48. It was a stifling hot day and a man fainted in the middle of a busy intersection. Traffic quickly piled up in all directions while a woman rushed to help him. When she knelt down to loosen his collar, a man emerged from the crowd, pushed her aside, and said, "It's all right honey, I've had a course in first aid."

The woman stood up and watched as he took the ill man's pulse and prepared to administer artificial respiration. At this point she tapped him on the shoulder and said, "When you get to the part about calling a doctor, I'm already here."

49. CREATIVE PROBLEM SOLVING:
According to a radio report, a middle school in Oregon was faced with a unique problem. A number of girls were beginning to use lipstick and would put it on in the bathroom. That was fine, but after they put on their lipstick they would press their lips to the mirror leaving dozens of little lip prints.

Finally the principal decided that something had to be done. She called all the girls to the bathroom and met them there with the custodian. She explained that all these lip prints were causing a major problem for the custodian who had to clean the mirrors every day. To demonstrate how difficult it was to clean the mirrors, she asked the custodian to clean one of the mirrors. He took out a long-handled brush, dipped it into the toilet and scrubbed the mirror.

Since then there have been no lip prints on the mirror.

50. Can you guess? See below and don't peek unless you give up...... When asked this riddle, 80% of kindergarten students got the answer, compared to 17% of Stanford

The poor have it,
The rich need it,
And if you eat it, you'll die?
the answer is........ ... ... Nothing

51. Three Wise Women. You DO know what would have happened if there would have been 3 wise WOMEN instead of 3 wise men don't you? They would have asked directions, arrived on time, helped deliver the baby, cleaned up the stable, made a casserole, and brought disposable diapers as a gift.

52. John invited his mother over for dinner. During the meal, his mother couldn't help but notice how beautiful John's roommate was. She had long been suspicious of a relationship between John and

his roommate and this only made her more curious. Over the course of the evening, while watching the two interact, she started to wonder if there was indeed more between John and the roommate than met the eye. Reading his mom's thoughts, John volunteered, "I know what you must be thinking, but I assure you, Julie and I are just roommates."

About a week later, Julie came to John and said, "Ever since your mother came to dinner, I've been unable to find the beautiful silver gravy ladle. You don't suppose she took it, do you?"

John said, "Well, I doubt it, but I'll write her a letter just to be sure." So he sat down and wrote: "Dear Mother, I'm not saying you 'did' take a gravy ladle from my house, and I'm not saying you 'did not' take a gravy ladle. But the fact remains that one has been missing ever since you were here for dinner."

Several days later, John received a letter from his mother which read: "Dear Son, I'm not saying that you 'do' sleep with Julie, and I'm not saying that you 'do not' sleep with Julie, but the fact remains that if she was sleeping in her own bed, she would have found the gravy ladle by now. Love, Mom"

53. A patrolman noticed a car of older women was going extremely slow. After following them for awhile he finally stopped them. While talking to the driver he noticed that the 3 women in the back and the passenger in the front were almost pressed back to their seats. He informed the woman driving that it was as dangerous to drive too slow as it was too fast. She responded ,"But officer I was going the speed limit." He said, "No, ma'am, you were going too slow." She said, "But I just saw the sign back there, 22." He said, "Oh, lady, that is the highway route, number 22. You were going the route number instead of the speed limit. By the way what is the problem with your passengers?" She responded "Oh, I'm am not sure but we just left highway 119."

54. When conducting a retreat for minister's wives a recent widow approached to share the following story with me. Her friend Ethel had also been widowed after a long marriage. Maria knew that Ethel and Henry had not had a lot of money so was very surprised

Ethel was wearing such a big new diamond ring. She asked Ethel, "where did you get such a ring?" Ethel responded, "Well after Henry was gone I went through his files. There in an envelope was several thousands dollars with a note, 'After I'm gone buy a big stone.'"

55. An elderly man went into a woman's room at the nursing home and said, "I bet you can't guess my age." She responded, "Well, turn around and I'll figure it out." Well he turned around and she said, "Oh, I meant without any of your clothes. And turn around 3 times really slow. He shed all his clothes then slowly turned around three times. When he stopped she said, "You are 82 years old." Amazed the man asked, "How did you figure it out?" She answered, "You told me at breakfast."

56. "JUST HER SIZE"
I believe that, in general, women are saner than men. For example, If you see people who have paid good money to stand in an out-door stadium on a freezing December day wearing nothing on the upper halves of their bodies except paint, those people will be male. Without males, there would be no such sport as professional lawn-mower racing. Also, there would be a 100 decline in the annual number of deaths related to efforts to shoot beer cans off of heads. Also, if women were in charge of all the world's nations, there would be, I sincerely believe this, virtually no military conflicts, and if there were a military conflict, everybody involved would feel just awful and there would soon be a high- level exchange of thoughtful notes written on greeting cards with flowers on the front, followed by a Peace Luncheon (which would be salads, with the dressing on the side).

So I sincerely believe that women are wiser than men, with the exception of one key area, and that area is: clothing sizes. In this particular area, women are insane.
When a man shops for clothes, his primary objective is to purchase clothes that fit on his particular body. A man will try on a pair of pants, and if those pants are too small, he'll try on a larger pair, and

when he finds a pair that fits, he buys them. Most men do not spend a lot of time fretting about the size of their pants. Many men wear jeans with the size printed right on the back label, so that if you're standing behind a man in a supermarket line, you can read his waist and inseam size. A man could have, say, a 52-inch waist and a 30-inch inseam, and his label will proudly display this information, which is basically the same thing as having a sign that says: "Howdy! My butt is the size of a Federal Express truck!" The situation is very different with women.

When a woman shops for clothes, her primary objective is NOT to find clothes that fit her particular body. She would like for that to be the case, but her primary objective is to purchase clothes that are the size she wore when she was 19 years old. This will be some arbitrary number such as "5" or "7." Don't ask me "5" or "7" of what; that question has baffled scientists for centuries. All I know is that if a woman was a size 5 at age 19, she wants to be a size 5 now, and if a size 5 outfit does not fit her, she will not move on to a larger size: She can't! Her size is 5! So she will keep trying on size 5 items, and unless they start fitting her, she will become extremely unhappy.

She may take this unhappiness out on her husband, who is waiting patiently in the mall, perhaps browsing in the Sharper Image store, trying to think of how he could justify purchasing a pair of night-vision binoculars. "Hi!" he'll say, when his wife finds him. "You know how sometimes the electricity goes out at night and..." "Am I fat?" she'll ask, cutting him off. This is a very bad situation for the man, because if he answers "yes," she'll be angry because he's saying that she's fat, and if he answers "no," she'll be angry because HE'S OBVIOUSLY LYING BECAUSE NONE OF THE SIZE 5's FIT HER.

There is no escape for the husband. I think a lot of unexplained disappearances occur because guys in malls see their wives unsuccessfully trying on outfits, and they realize their lives will be easier if, before their wives come out and demand to know whether they're fat, the guys just run off and join a UFO cult.

The other day my wife was in a terrific mood, and you know why? Because she had successfully put on a size 6 outfit. She said this made her feel wonderful. She said, and this is a direct quote: "I wouldn't care if these pants were this big (here she held her arms far apart) as long as they have a '6' on them."

Here's how you could get rich: Start a women's clothing store called "SIZE 2," in which all garments, including those that were originally intended to be restaurant awnings, had labels with the words "SIZE 2." I bet you'd sell clothes like crazy. You'd probably get rich, and you could retire, maybe take up some philanthropic activity to benefit humanity. I'm thinking here of professional lawn mower racing.

57. Element: Woman
Symbol: Wo
Discoverer: Adam
Atomic Weight: accepted as 118 but is known to vary from 100 to 300 lbs.
Occurrence: surplus quantities in all urban areas
Physical Properties:
    1)   surface usually covered in painted film
    2)   boils at nothing, freezes without reason
    3)   melts if given proper treatment
    4)   bitter if used incorrectly
    5)   found in various states, ranging from virgin metal, to common 'ore
Chemical Properties:
  1) possess great affinity for gold, silver, platinum and precious stones
  2) able to absorb great quantities of expensive substances
  3) may explode spontaneously if left alone with a male
  4) insoluble in liquids but activity greatly increased by saturation in alcohol
  5) yields to pressure applied to correct points
Uses:
  1) highly ornamental, especially in sports cars
  2) most powerful money-reducing agent known
  3) can be a great aid to relaxation

Tests:
1) pure specimen turns rosy tint if discovered in natural state
2) turns green if placed beside a better specimen
Caution:
1) highly dangerous except in experienced hands
2) illegal to posses more than one except in certain states   (ex. Utah).

58. TRUE STORY: Carjacking Foiled
An elderly lady did her shopping and, upon return, found four males in her car. She dropped her shopping bags and drew her handgun, proceeding to scream at them at the top of her voice that she knows how to use it and that she will if required: so get out of the car.

The four men didn't wait around for a second invitation but got out and ran like mad, whereupon the lady proceeded to load her shopping bags into the back of the car and get into the drivers seat. Small problem, her key wouldn't fit the ignition. Her car was identical and parked four or five spaces farther down.

She loaded her bags into her car and drove to the police station. The sergeant to whom she told the story nearly fell off his chair with laughter and pointed to the other end of the counter, where four pale white males were reporting a carjacking by a mad elderly white woman: no charges were filed.

59. One winter a Priest and a nun were traveling across the country and arrived late at a hotel. They were distressed to find that there was only one room left to rent. They both told the innkeeper that he would have to find them separate rooms. The innkeeper said that he was sorry but only the one room was available but it did have two double beds. Finally they agreed to stay in the same room. After they had been in their separate beds for awhile the Priest said, "Sister, I'm cold can you please get up and find me a blanket." So the Sister got up and found the Priest a blanket. A few minutes later the Priest said that he was still cold and would the Sister please find him another blanket. The Sister got up and found another blan-

ket. About 15 minutes later the Priest said, "Sister, I am still so very cold. For this night, couldn't we pretend that we are married?" The sister replied, "Oh, yes, Father, that would be an excellent idea." The Priest said, "Well I am still cold so . . ." The Sister said, "Then get up and find your own blanket!"

60. A man is like fine wine. He starts out raw as grapes and it is a woman's job to stomp on him and keep him in the dark until he matures into something she'd like to have dinner with.

Jokes for Everyone

1. Ole and Lena are sitting down to their usual cup of morning coffee listening to the weather report coming over the radio. "There will be 3 to 5 inches of snow today and a snow emergency has been declared. You must park your cars on the odd numbered side of the streets." Ole gets up from his coffee and replies, "Jeez, O.K."

Two days later, again they both are sitting down with their cups of coffee and the weather forecast is: "There will be 2 to 4 inches of snow today and a snow emergency has been declared. You must park your cars on the even numbered side of the streets." Ole gets up from his coffee and replies, "Jeez, O.K."

Three days later, again they both are sitting down with their cups of coffee and the weather forecast is: "There will be 6 to 8 inches of now today and a snow emergency has been declared. You must park your cars on the. . ." and then the power goes out and Ole doesn't get the rest of the instructions.

He says to Lena, "Jeez, what am I going to do now Lena?"

Lena replies, "Aw, Ole, just leave the car in the garage."

2. The Washington Post's "Style Invitational" asked readers to take any word from the dictionary, alter it by adding, subtracting or changing one letter, and supply a new definition. Here are some recent winners:

Reintarnation: Coming back to life as a hillbilly.

Foreploy: Any misrepresentation about yourself for the purpose of obtaining sex.

Giraffiti: Vandalism spray-painted very, very high. . . .

Tatyr: A lecherous Mr. Potato Head.

Sarchasm: The gulf between the author of sarcastic wit and the recipient who doesn't get it.

Inoculatte: To take coffee intravenously when you are running late.

Hipatitis: Terminal coolness.

Osteopornosis: A degenerate disease.

Burglesque: A poorly planned break-in. (See: Watergate)
Karmageddon: It's like, when everybody is sending off all these really bad vibes, right? And then, like, the Earth explodes and it's like a serious bummer.
Glibido: All talk and no action.
Dopeler effect: The tendency of stupid ideas to seem smarter when they come at you rapidly.
Intaxication: Euphoria at getting a refund from the IRS, which lasts until you realize it was your money to start with.

3. If you receive e-mail, it's wise to remember how easily this wonderful technology can be misused, sometimes unintentionally, with serious consequences. Consider the case of the Illinois man who left the snow-filled street of Chicago for a vacation in Florida. His wife was on a business trip and was planning to meet him there the next day. When he reached his hotel, he decided to send his wife a quick e-mail. Unable to find the scrap of paper on which he had written her e-mail address, he did his best to type it in from memory. Unfortunately, he missed one letter, and his note was directed instead to an elderly preacher's wife, whose husband had passed away only the day before. When the grieving widow checked her e-mail, she took one look at the monitor, let out a piercing scream, and fell to the floor in a dead faint. At the sound, her family rushed into the room and saw this note on the screen:
Dearest Wife,
Just got checked in. Everything prepared for your arrival tomorrow. PS. Sure is hot down here!

4. A young woman, (a new teacher) was giving an assignment to her Grade 6 class one day. It was a large assignment so she started writing high up on the chalkboard. Suddenly there was a giggle from one of the male students. She quickly turned and asked, "What's so funny Pat?"
"Well teacher, I just saw one of your garters."
"Get out of my classroom," she yells, "I don't want to see you for three days." The teacher turns back to the chalkboard. Realizing

she had forgotten to title the assignment; she reaches to the very top of the chalkboard. Suddenly there is an even louder giggle from another male student. She quickly turns and asks, "What's so funny Billy?" "Well teacher, I just saw both of your garters." Again she yells, "Get out of my classroom!" This time the punishmentIs more severe, "I don't want to see you for three weeks." Embarrassed and frustrated, she drops the eraser when she turns around again. So she bends over to pick it up. This time there is an all out laugh from another male student. She quickly turns to see Little Johnny leaving the classroom. "Where do you think you are going?" she asks. "Well teacher, from what I just saw, my school days are over!"

5. A Russian couple was walking down the street in Moscow one night, when the man felt a drop hit his nose. "I think it's raining" he said to his wife. "No, that felt more like snow to me" she replied.
"No, I'm sure it was just rain" he said.
Well, as these things go, they were about to have a major argument about whether it was raining or snowing. Just then, they saw a minor communist party official walking toward them. "Let's not fight about it," the man said, "Let's ask Comrade Rudolph whether it's officially raining or snowing".
As the official approached, the man said, "Tell us, Comrade Rudolph, is it officially raining or snowing?"
"It's raining, of course", he replied, and walked on.
But the woman insisted: "I know that felt like snow!"
The man quietly replied: "Rudolph the Red knows rain, dear!"

6. Top Ten Signs That You Are Burned Out Because Of Work:
10. You're so tired you now answer the phone, "Hell."
9. Your friends call to ask how you've been, and you immediately scream, "Get off my back, b!?@! <mailto:b!?@!> "
8. Your garbage can IS your "in" box.
7. You wake up to discover your bed is on fire, but go back to sleep because you just don't care.
6. You have so much on your mind, you've forgotten how to eat.

5. Visions of the upcoming weekend help you make it through Monday.

4. You don't set your alarm anymore cause you know the pager will go off before the alarm does.

3. You leave for a party and instinctively bring your ID badge.

2. Your Day Timer exploded a week ago.

And the number one sign that you are burned out because of work is.........

1. You think about how relaxing it would be if you were in jail.

7. 25 Snappy Comebacks To The Question ...
"Why aren't you married yet?"

1. You haven't asked yet.
2. I was hoping to do something meaningful with my life.
3. What? And spoil my great sex life?
4. Nobody would believe me in white.
5. Because I just love hearing this question.
6. Just lucky, I guess.
7. It gives my parents something to live for.
8. My fiancee is awaiting parole.
9. I'm still hoping for a shot at Miss America.
10. Do you know how hard it is to get two tickets to Miss Saigon?
11. I'm waiting until I get to be your age.
12. It didn't seem worth a blood test.
13. I already have enough laundry to do, thank you.
14. Because it would take all the spontaneity out of dating.
15. My co-op board doesn't allow spouses.
16. I'd have to forfeit my billion dollar trust fund.
17. They just opened a great singles bar on my block.
18. I wouldn't want my parents to drop dead from sheer happiness.
19. I guess it just goes to prove that you can't trust those voodoo doll rituals.
20. What? And lose all the money I've invested in running personal ads?
21. We really want to, but my lover's husband just won't go for it.

22. I don't want to have to support another person on my paycheck.
23. Why aren't you thin?
24. I'm married to my career, although recently we have been considering a trial separation.
25. (Bonus reply ... for single moms) Because having a husband and a child would be redundant.

8.   How many members of your sign does it take to Change A Light Bulb?

Aries: Just one. You want to make something of it?

Taurus: One, but just "try" to convince them that the burned-out bulb is useless and should be thrown away.

Gemini: Two, but the job never gets done - they just keep arguing about who is supposed to do it and how it's supposed to be done!

Cancer: Just one. But it takes a therapist three years to help them through the grief process.

Leo: Leo's don't change light bulbs, although sometimes their agent will get a Virgo to do the job for them while they're out.

Virgo: Approximately 1.0000000 with an error of +/- 1 millionth.

Libra: Eh, two. Or maybe one. No - on second thought, make that two. Is that okay with you?

Scorpio: That information is strictly secret and shared only with the Enlightened Ones in the Star Chamber of the Ancient Hierarchical Order.

Sagittarius: The sun is shining, the day is young and we've got our whole lives ahead of us, and you're inside worrying about a stupid light bulb?

Capricorn: I don't waste my time with these childish jokes.

Aquarius: Well, you have to remember that everything is energy, so...

Pisces: Light bulb? What light bulb?

9. Signs that you have had too much of the '90s

* Cleaning up the dining area means getting the fast-food bags out of the back seat of your car.

* Your reason for not staying in touch with family is that they do

not have e-mail addresses.
* Keeping up with sports entails adding ESPN's home page to your bookmarks.
* You have a "to do" list that includes entries for lunch and bathroom breaks, and they are the ones that never get crossed off.
* You have actually faxed your Christmas list to your parents
* Pick-up lines now include a reference to liquid assets and capital gains.
* You consider second-day air delivery painfully slow.
* You assume the question "to valet-park or not" is rhetorical.
* You refer to your dining-room table as the flat filing cabinet.
*Your idea of being organized is multiple-colored post-it notes.
* Your grocery list has been on your refrigerator so long some of the products don't even exist any more.
* You lecture the neighborhood kids selling lemonade on ways to improve their process.
* You get all excited when it's Saturday and you can wear sweats to work.
* You refer to the tomatoes grown in your garden as deliverables.
* You find you really need PowerPoint to explain what you do for a living.
* You normally eat out of vending machines and at the most expensive restaurant in town -- in the same week.
* You think that "progressing an action plan" and "calendarizing a project" are acceptable English phrases
* You know the people at the airport hotels better than you know your next-door neighbors.
* You ask your friends to "think outside of the box" when making Friday night plans.
* You think Einstein would have been more effective if he had put his ideas into a matrix.
You think a "half day" means leaving at 5 o'clock.
 And the number one sign you've had way too much of the '90's..
* You get most of your jokes in e-mail instead of in person.

10. Grandma: My grandmother has a bumper sticker on her car

that says, 'Sexy Senior Citizen'. You don't want to think of your grandmother that way, do you? Out there entering wet shawl contests. Makes you wonder where she got that dollar she gave you for your birthday

11. Ads in Bills: Have you ever noticed that they put advertisements in with your bills now? Like bills aren't distasteful enough, they have to stuff junk mail in there with them. I get back at them. I put garbage in with my check when I mail it in. Coffee grinds, banana peels... I write, "Could you throw this away for me, please? Thank you."

12. Fabric Softener: My wife uses fabric softener. I never knew what that stuff was for. Then I noticed women were coming up to me (sniff) 'Married' (walked off). That's how they mark their territory. You can take off that ring, but it's hard to get that April fresh scent out of your clothes.

13. Morning Differences: Men and women are different in the morning. The men wake up aroused in the morning. We can't help it. We just wake up and we want you. And the women are thinking, 'how can he want me the way I look in the morning?' It's because we can't see you. We have no blood anywhere near our optic nerve.

14. How old are you???
To get an idea of the lives of those entering college this fall, read on..... and try not to laugh..............or cry . . . .
1. The people who are starting college this fall across the nation were born in 1980.
2. They have no meaningful recollection of the Reagan era, and did not know he had ever been shot.
3. They were prepubescent when the Persian Gulf War was waged.
4. Black Monday 1987 is as significant to them as the Great Depression.
5. There has only been one Pope. They can only really remember one president.

6. They were 11 when the Soviet Union broke apart, and do not remember the Cold War.

7. They have never feared a nuclear war.

8. "The Day After" is a pill to them, not a movie.

9. They are too young to remember the Space shuttle blowing up, and Tienamin Square means nothing to them.

10. Their lifetime has always included AIDS.

11. They never had a Polio shot, and likely, do not know what it is.

12. Bottle caps have not only always been screw off, but have always been plastic. They have no idea what a pull top can looks like.

13. Atari predates them, as do vinyl albums.

14. The expression "you sound like a broken record" means nothing to them.

15. They have never owned a record player.

16. They have likely never played Pac Man, and have never heard of Pong.

17. Star Wars looks very fake to them.

18. There have always been red M&M's, and blue ones are not new. What do you mean there used to be beige ones?

19. They may have heard of an 8-track, but chances are they probably have never actually seen or heard one.

20. The Compact Disc was introduced when they were 1 year old.

21. As far as they know, stamps have always cost about 32 cents.

22. They have always had an answering machine.

23. Most have never seen a TV set with only 13 channels, nor have they seen a black and white TV.

24. They have always had cable.

25. There have always been VCR's, but they have no idea what Beta is.

26. They cannot fathom not having a remote control.

27. They were born the year that Walkmen were introduced by Sony.

28. Roller-skating has always meant inline for them.

29. The Tonight Show has always been with Jay Leno.

30. They have no idea when or why Jordache jeans were cool.

31. Popcorn has always been cooked in a microwave.
32. They have never seen Larry Bird play, and Kareem Abdul-Jabbar is a Football player.
33. They never took a swim and thought about Jaws.
34. The Vietnam War is as ancient history to them as WWI, WWII or even the Civil War.
35. They have no idea that Americans were ever held hostage in Iran.
36. They can't imagine what hard contact lenses are.
37. They don't know who Mork was or where he was from.
38. They never heard the terms "Where's the beef?", "I'd Walk a mile for a Camel," or "de plane, de plane!".
39. They don't know 'who shot J.R.' and have no idea who J.R. is.
40. The Titanic was found? I thought we always knew where it was.
41. Michael Jackson has always been white.
42. Kansas, Chicago, Boston, America, and Alabama are places, not groups.
43. McDonalds never came in Styrofoam containers.

15. One summer evening during a violent thunderstorm a mother was tucking her small boy into bed. She was about to turn off the light when he asked with a tremor in his voice, "Mommy, will you sleep with me tonight?" The mother smiled and gave him a reassuring hug. "I can't dear," she said. "I have to sleep in Daddy's room."

A long silence was broken at last by a shaken little voice saying, "The big sissy."

16. Bumper Stickers
1. Everyone has a photographic memory. Some don't have film.
2. He who laughs last, thinks slowest.
3. A day without sunshine is like, well, night.
4. On the other hand, you have different fingers.
5. Change is inevitable, except from a vending machine.
6. Back up my hard drive? How do I put it in reverse?

7. I just got lost in thought. It was unfamiliar territory.
8. When the chips are down, the buffalo is empty.
9. Seen it all, done it all, can't remember most of it.
10. Those who live by the sword get shot by those who don't.
11. I feel like I'm diagonally parked in a parallel universe.
12. He's not dead, he's electroencephalographically challenged.
13. She's always late. Her ancestors arrived on the Juneflower.
14. You have the right to remain silent. Anything you say will be misquoted, then used against you.
15. I wonder how much deeper the ocean would be without sponges.
16. Honk if you love peace and quiet.
17. Pardon my driving, I am reloading.
18. Despite the cost of living, have you noticed how it remains so popular?
19. Nothing is fool-proof to a sufficiently talented fool.

17. A guy walks into a post office one day to see a middle-aged, balding man standing at the counter methodically placing "Love" stamps on bright pink envelopes with hearts all over them. He then takes out a perfume bottle and starts spraying scent all over them.
 His curiosity getting the better of him, he goes up to the balding man and asks him what he is doing. The man says "I'm sending out 1,000 Valentine cards signed, 'Guess who?'" "But why?" asks the man. "I'm a divorce lawyer," the man replies.

18. Four expectant fathers were in Minneapolis hospital waiting room, while their wives were in labor.
 The nurse arrived and announced to the first man, "Congratulations sir, You're the father of twins."
 "What a coincidence" the man said with some obvious pride. "I work for the Minnesota Twins baseball team."
 The nurse returned in a little while and turned to the second man, "You sir, are the father of triplets."
 "Wow, That's really an incredible coincidence " he answered. "I work for the 3M Corporation." My buddies at work will never let me live this one down.

An hour later, while the other two men were passing cigars around, the nurse came back, this time she turn to the 3rd man - who had been quiet in the corner. She announced that his wife had just given birth to quadruplets.

Stunned, he barely could reply. "Don't tell me! Another coincidence?" asked the nurse. After finally regaining his composure, he said "I don't believe it, I work for the Four Seasons Hotel."

After hearing this, everybody's attention turned to the 4th guy, who had just fainted, flat out on the floor. The nurse rushed to his side and after some time, he slowly gained back his consciousness. When he was finally able to speak, you could hear him whispering repeatedly the same phrase over and over again. "I should have never taken that job at 7-Eleven... "I should have never taken that job at 7-Eleven..."I should have never taken that job at 7-Eleven..."

19. Retirement Wisdom

A wise old gentleman retired and purchased a modest home near a junior high school. He spent the first few weeks of his retirement in peace and contentment - then a new school year began.

The very next afternoon three young boys, full of youthful, after-school enthusiasm, came down his street, beating merrily on every trash can they encountered. The crashing percussion continued day after day, until finally the wise old man decided it was time to take some action.

The next afternoon, he walked out to meet the young percussionists as they banged their way down the street. Stopping them, he said, "You kids are a lot of fun. I like to see you express your exuberance like that. Used to do the same thing when I was your age. Will you do me a favor? I'll give you each a dollar if you'll promise to come around every day and do your thing."

The kids were elated and continued to do a bang-up job on the trash cans. After a few days, the old-timer greeted the kids again, but this time he had a sad smile on his face. "This recession's really putting a dent in my income," he told them. "From now on, I'll only be able to pay you 50 cents to beat on the cans."

The noisemakers were obviously displeased, but they did accept his offer and continued their afternoon ruckus.

A few days later, the wily retiree approached them again as they drummed their way down the street. "Look," he said, "I haven't received my Social Security check yet, so I'm not going to be able to give you more than 25 cents. Will that be okay?"

"A lousy quarter?" the drum leader exclaimed. "If you think we're going to waste our time, beating these cans around for a quarter, you're nuts! No way, mister. We quit!"

And the old man enjoyed peace and serenity for the rest of his days.

20. Upon entering the little country store, the stranger noticed a sign saying; DANGER! BEWARE OF DOG! posted on the glass door. Inside he noticed a harmless old hound dog asleep on the floor besides the cash register. He asked the store manager, "Is THAT the dog folks are supposed to beware of?" "Yep, that's him," he replied. The stranger couldn't help but be amused. "That certainly doesn't look like a dangerous dog to me. Why in the world would you post that sign?"

"Because," the owner replied, "before I posted that sign, people kept tripping over him."

21. In the back woods of Arkansas, Mr. Stewart's wife went into labor in the middle of the night, and the doctor was called out to assist in the delivery. To keep the nervous father-to-be busy, the doctor handed him a lantern and said, "Here, you hold this high so I can see what I'm doing."

Soon, a wee baby boy was brought into the world. "Whoa there Scotty!" said the doctor. "Don't be in a rush to put the lantern down...I think there's yet another wee one to come."

Sure enough, within minutes he had delivered another little baby.

"No, no, don't be in a great hurry to be putting down that lantern, young man...It seems there's yet another one besides!" cried the doctor.

The new father scratched his head in bewilderment, and asked the doctor. "Do ye think it's the light that's attractin' them?"

22. A man drives to a gas station and has his tank filled up. While doing this the clerk spots two penguins sitting on the back seat of the car. He asks the driver, "What's up with the penguins in the back seat?" The man in the car says, "I found them. I asked myself what to do with them but, I haven't a clue."

The clerk ponders a bit then says, "You should take them to the zoo." "Yeah, that's a good idea," says the man in the car and drives away.

The next day the man with the car is back at the same gas station. The clerk sees the penguins are still in the back seat of the car. "Hey, they're still here! I thought you were going to take them to the zoo!" "Oh, I did," says the driver, "and we had a swell time. Today I'm taking them to the beach."

23. A single man wanted someone to help him with the household chores, so he decided to get a pet to help out. He went to the local pet shop and asks the owner for advice on a suitable animal. The owner suggested a dog, but the man said, "Nah, dogs can't do dishes." The owner then suggested a cat, but the man said, "Nah, cats can't do the ironing." Finally the owner suggests a centipede, "This is the perfect pet for you. It can do anything!" OK, the man thought, I'll give it a try, so he bought it and took it home. Once home he told the centipede to wash the dishes. The centipede looks over and there are piles and piles of dirty dishes that look to be a month old. Five minutes later, all the pots are washed, dried and put away. Great, thought the man. Now he told the centipede to do the dusting and vacuuming. 15 minutes later the house is spotless. Wow, thought the man, so he decided to try another idea. "Go down to the corner and get me the evening paper," he told the centipede, and off it went. 15 minutes later, the centipede hadn't returned. 30 minutes later and still no centipede. 45 minutes and the man was sick of waiting, so he got up and went out to look for the centipede. As he opened the front door, there on the step was the centipede. "Hey, what cha' doing there? I sent you out for the paper 45 minutes ago and now I find you out here without the paper! What gives?" "Hold on a minute!" said the centipede, "I'm still putting on

my darn boots!!!"

24. You know you are getting old when:
Doctor to patient: I have good news and bad news: the good news is that you are not a hypochondriac.
It's hard to be nostalgic when you can't remember anything.
You know you're getting old when you stop buying green bananas.
Death is not the end; there remains the litigation over the estate.
My uncle reads the obits every day. He can't understand how people always die in alphabetical order.\ Last Will and Testament: Being of sound mind, I spent all my money.

25. Business signs:
On a scientist's door: "Gone Fission"
On a taxidermist's window: "We really know our stuff"
Outside a Hotel: "Help, we need inn-experienced people."
At an Auto Body Shop: "May we have the next dents?"
In a Beauty Shop: "Dye now!"
At a music store: "Out to lunch. Bach at 12:30. Offen bach sooner."
On a music teacher's door: "Out Chopin"
At a farmers field: "The farmer allows walkers to cross the field for free but the bull charges."
In a Podiatrist's window: "Time wounds all heels"
At the Electric Company: "We would be delighted if you send in your bill. However, if you don't, you will be."
At a muffler shop: "Our work is exhausting."

26. Two children, age six, a boy and girl, were best friends. Their parents did not want them to play together because the little boy was Catholic and the little girl, Protestant. Every now and then they would elude their parents. One day they met down by the local swimming hole to go swimming. They didn't have their suits so they decided to skinny dip. After disrobing, the little boy looked at the little girl and said, "So that's the difference between Catholics and Protestants!"

27. New Orleans lawyer sought an FHA loan for a client. He was told the loan would be granted if he could prove satisfactory title to a parcel of property being offered as collateral. The title to the property dated back to 1803, which took the lawyer three months to track down.

After sending the information to the FHA, he received the following reply (actual letter):

"Upon review of your letter adjoining your client's loan application, we note that the request is supported by an Abstract of Title. While we compliment the able manner in which you have prepared and presented the application, we must point out that you have only cleared title to the proposed collateral back to 1803. Before final approval can be accorded, it will be necessary to clear the title back to its origin."

Annoyed, the lawyer responded as follows (actual letter):

"Your letter regarding title in Case No. 189156 has been received. I note that you wish to have title extended further than the 194 years covered by the present application.

I was unaware that any educated person in this country, particularly those working in the property area, would not know that Louisiana was purchased by the U. S. from France in 1803, the year of origin identified in our application. For the edification of uninformed FHA bureaucrats, the title to the land prior to U. S. ownership was obtained from France, which had acquired it by Right of Conquest from Spain. The land came into possession of Spain by Right of Discovery made in the year 1492 by a sea captain named Christopher Columbus, who had been granted the privilege of seeking a new route to India by the then reigning monarch, Isabella. The good queen, being a pious woman and careful about titles, almost as much as the FHA, took the precaution of securing the blessing of the Pope before she sold her jewels to fund Columbus' expedition. Now the Pope, as I'm sure you know, is the emissary of Jesus Christ, the Son of God. And God, it is commonly accepted, created this world. Therefore, I believe it is safe to presume that He also made that part of the world called Louisiana. He, therefore, would be the owner of origin. I hope ...you find His original claim

to be satisfactory.
Now, may we have our ... loan?"

28. COSEC ORGANIZATIONAL LEAVE POLICY (SICKNESS, VACATION, HOLIDAYS, ETC)

SICKNESS: No excuse. We no longer accept your doctor's statement as proof, as we believe that if you are able to go to the doctor, you are able to come to work.

DEATH (Other than your own): This is no excuse. There is nothing you can do for them and we are sure someone in a lesser position can tend to the arrangements. However, IF the funeral can be held in the late afternoon, we will be glad to let you off 10 minutes early, PROVIDED that your share of the work is ahead enough to keep the job going in your absence.

DEATH (Your own): It will be accepted as an excuse but we would like a two-week notice, as we feel it is your duty to teach someone else your job.

LEAVE OF ABSENCE (For an operation): We no longer allow this practice. We wish to discourage any thought you may have about needing an operation. We believe that as long as you are employed here, you will need all of whatever you have and should not consider having anything removed. We hired you as you are, and to have anything removed would certainly make you less than we bargained for.

REST ROOM POLICY: Too much time is being spent in the restrooms. In the future, we will follow the practice of going to the restroom in alphabetical order. For instance, those whose names begin with "A" will go from 8:00 a.m. to 8:02 a.m. "B" will go from 8:05 a.m. to 8:07 a.m., and so on. If you are unable to go at your time, it will be necessary to wait until the next day when your turn comes again.

VACATION: Vacations are allowed, but are strongly discouraged as they do not reflect an attitude of absolute loyalty. Should you feel the need for a vacation due to family, peers, social pressure, etc., please try to arrange these at least two years in advance and have all your work caught up in advance of the time you will be out of the office. Further discussion on this very distasteful subject is also discouraged.

HOLIDAYS: This organization feels that the term "Holiday" has been misused by the state and federal government. There are presently ten legal holidays which we recognize. We will only observe them if and when they fall on a Sunday (this excludes December 25 obviously since we also believe in Motherhood and apple pie.) We want you to be a happy employee within this organization. Since productivity is our ultimate purpose, it is felt the above guidelines will help increase productivity and therefore overall organizational happiness. If you have any suggestions for making our policy more effective and efficient, please contact your supervisor.

29. A lady goes to her parish priest one day and tells him, "Father, I have a problem. I have two female parrots but they only know how to say one thing."
"What do they say?" the priest inquired. "They say, 'Hi, we're prostitutes. Do you want to have some fun?'" "That's obscene!" the priest exclaimed, "I can see why you are embarrassed." He thought a minute and then said, "You know, I may have a solution to this problem. I have two male parrots whom I have taught to pray and read the Bible. Bring your two parrots over to my house and we will put them in the cage with my parrots Francis and Thomas. Francis and Thomas can teach your parrots to pray and worship. I'm sure your parrots will stop saying that phrase in no time."
"Thank you," the woman responded, "this may very well be the solution." The next day, she brought her female parrots to the priest's house. As he ushered her in, she saw his two male parrots inside their cage, holding their rosary beads and praying. Impressed, she

walked over and placed her Parrots in with them. After just a couple of seconds, the female parrots exclaimed out in unison, "Hi, we're prostitutes. Do you want to have some fun?"

There was a stunned silence. Finally, one male parrot looked over at the other male parrot and said, "Put the beads away, Francis, our prayers have been answered!"

30. Two men go into a local diner for lunch. As they read the menu the waitress comes over and asks them, "You ready to order?"

The first man replies, "Yes, I'd like a quickie."

The waitress is astonished, slaps the man and exclaims, "A quickie? Sir, we don't talk like that in here." And walks off.

The man looked stunned and pointing to the menu said, "I just wanted to order that."

The other man said "I think it's pronounced Quiche."

A man on the track told that joke one morning and another man said, "I don't get it. What's a Quiche?"

31. A young boy went up to his father and asked, "What is the difference between potentially and realistically?" The father answered, " Go ask your mother if she would sleep with Robert Redford for a million dollars. Also, ask your sister if she would sleep with Brad Pitt for a million dollars. Come back and tell me what you have learned." So the boy went to his mother and said, "Would you sleep with Robert Redford for a million dollars?" The mother replied, "Of course I would!! I wouldn't pass up an opportunity like that."

The boy then went to his sister and said," Would you sleep with Brad Pitt for a million dollars?" The girl replied, "Oh my God! I'd be nuts to pass that up!!"

The boy then thought about it for two or three days and went back to his dad. His father asked him, "Did you find out the difference between potential and realistic?"

"Yes," replied the boy, "potentially we're sitting on two million dollars but realistically we're living with two sluts !!!"

32. A friend of mine asked his wife if she would sleep with Robert Redford for a millions dollars. Her reply, "Oh, my yes, but where are we going to come up with the million dollars?"

33. * So many stupid people . . . so few comets.
* Your kid may be an honors student, but you're still an idiot.
* All generalizations are false.
* Cover me. I'm changing lanes.
* I brake for no apparent reason.
* I'm not as think as you drunk I am.
* Forget about World Peace . Visualize using your turn signal.
* We have enough youth, how about a fountain of Smart?
* He who laughs last thinks slowest.
* Lottery: A tax on people who are bad at math.
* It IS as bad as you think, and they ARE out to get you.
* Auntie Em, Hate you, hate Kansas, taking the dog. Dorothy.
* Change is inevitable, except from a vending machine.
* Time is what keeps everything from happening at once.
* Out of my mind. Back in five minutes.
* Forget the Joneses, I keep us up with the Simpsons.
* Born free . . . Taxed to death.
* The more people I meet, the more I like my dog.
* Laugh alone and the world thinks you're an idiot.
* I get enough exercise just pushing my luck.
* Work is for people who don't know how to fish.
* Montana-At least our cows are sane!
* I didn't fight my way to the top of the food chain to be a vegetarian.
* Women who seek to be equal to men lack ambition.
* If you don't like the news, go out and make some.
* When you do a good deed, get a receipt in case heaven is like the IRS.
* No radio-Already stolen.
* Real women don't have hot flashes, they have power surges.
* I took an IQ test and the results were negative.

* Where there's a will, I want to be in it.
* OK, who stopped payment on my reality check?
* Few women admit their age; Fewer men act it.
* I don't suffer from insanity, I enjoy every minute of it.
* Tell me to 'stuff it'-I'm a taxidermist.
* IRS: We've got what it takes to take what you've got.
* Time is the best teacher. Unfortunately, it kills all its students.
* It's lonely at the top, but you eat better.
* According to my calculations, the problem doesn't exist.
* Some people are only alive because it is illegal to kill.
* Pride is what we have. Vanity is what others have.
* A bartender is just a pharmacist with a limited inventory.
* Reality? Is that where the pizza delivery guy comes from?
* How can I miss you if you won't go away?
* Warning: Dates in calendar are closer than they appear.
* Give me ambiguity or give me something else.
* We are born naked, wet, and hungry. Then things get worse.
* Make it idiot-proof and someone will make a better idiot.
* Always remember you're unique, just like everyone else.
* Friends help you move. Real friends help you move bodies.
* Very funny Scotty, now beam down my clothes.
* Consciousness: That annoying time between naps.
* I souport publik edekashun.
* Be nice to your kids. They'll choose your nursing home.
* There are 3 kinds of people: those who can count & those who can't.
* Why is 'abbreviation' such a long word?
* Ever stop to think and forget to start again?
* Keep honking...I'm reloading.
* Caution: I drive like you do.
* My kid beat up your honor student!

34. Observations:

Motel mattresses are better on the side away from the phone.

Never kick a cow chip on a hot day.

There are two theories about arguin' with a woman. Neither one works.

When weeding, the best way to make sure you are removing a weed and not a valuable plant is to pull on it. If it comes out easily, it is a valuable plant.

One good turn gets most of the blankets.

Never lick a gift horse in the mouth.

It's always darkest before dawn (So if you're going to steal your neighbor's paper, that's the best time to do it!)

The second mouse gets the cheese.

The early worm gets eaten!

The sooner you fall behind, the more time you will have to catch up.

A truly wise man never plays leapfrog with a unicorn.

Remember, it's pillage first, burn second.

Never ever do card tricks for the group you play poker with.

Want to lose something? Put it in the washing machine with your socks.

35. One of the hardest things about writing a book is to go back and put mistakes in it. You don't want anyone to think you are perfect.

36. I once spotted a bumper sticker that read: "Nothing could be finer than to wake up with a Shriner." I inquired where on earth I could get one. The man said, "But you are not a Shriner." And I replied, "But I am a Schreiner!' He exclaimed, "oh, Oh, OH! OH, NO!"

37. The doctor awoke in a foul mood He complained to his wife that the breakfast was awful, the house was a mess. "Why you aren't even good in bed!" Later in the day he realized that he might have been too tacky so he called his wife. He asked, "What are you doing?" "Oh," she replied, "I'm in bed." He responded , "But

it's 11 o'clock." She said, "yes I know, but I'm getting a second opinion."

38. An American tourist looked over the rim into a volcanic crater. He turned to the guide, "Reminds one of hell, doesn't it?" The guide threw up his hands and exclaimed, "These Americans have been everywhere!'

39. Did you know that Tweety Bird is sick? He has chirpies. It's a canarial disease and untweetable.

40. After months of being pestered to give a testimonial from a pharmaceutical firm, the old man wrote. "I've been deaf for the last 12 years. After using your ointment for only two weeks, I heard from my brother in Idaho.

41. While out walking an old man heard a voice saying, "Kiss me mister and I'll turn into a beautiful woman and make your dreams come true." Looking around the only thing he saw was a frog. Again the frog said, "Kiss me mister and I'll turn into a beautiful woman and make your dreams come true." The man reached down, picked up the frog, put it in his pocket. Bewildered, the frog hollered, "Mister! Didn't you hear me?" The man replied, "At my age, a speaking frog is worth more!"

42. During a meeting where everyone was sitting close together someone remarked, "Well, I believe that someone's deodorant has stopped working." Another person spoke up, "It's not mine, because I don't use any!"

43. Birdie, Birdie, In that tree.
Why did you do that on me?
I'm no sissy, I will not cry.
But I sure am glad that cows don't fly!"

44. Some men were complaining how bad one of there buddies

snored and no one wanted to share a room with him on their hunting trip. One of the guys, Jeff, said he would. The next morning the man who snored staggered into the breakfast room looking like he hadn't slept at all. The guys later asked Jeff what he did, and how he slept. He replied, "Oh, I slept fine. Right before I turned off the light I leaned over to him and gave him a great big kiss. He was afraid to go to sleep."

45.   Hickory dickory dock.
The mouse ran up the clock
The clock struck one
And killed the darn thing.

46.   Little Miss Muffet
Sat on a tuffet
Eating her curds and whey.
Along came a spider
And sat down beside her
And asked, "What's in the bowl, Witch?"

47.   Mary had a little watch
She swallowed it one day.
The doctor gave her caster oil
To pass the time away.
The castor oil it did not work.
The watch she did not pass.
So if you want to know what time it is,
Just look up Mary's . . . Uncle
He has a watch just like it.

48.   Mary, Mary, quite contrary,
How does your garden grow?
With Silver bells and cockle shells
And one lonely Petunia.

49.   Jack and Jill went up the hill
Each of them had a quarter

Jill came down with 50 cents
I guess they didn't go after water.

50. An old man was sitting on a park bench crying his heart out. Another man came up and asked, "What's wrong?" The old man said, "OH, I married the most beautiful young woman last week. She loves me dearly and makes passionate love to me." Then why are you crying?" "Oh, I can't remember where I live!'

51. Paul was busy preparing a speech about sex for his Toastmasters Club. When his wife asked him what he was going to talk about he responded with, "Lasagna." He didn't want her to be upset or fear that he was going to say anything personal. A few days later she ran into Don, another member of that club. She commented she was surprised on Paul's subject. Don stated they were all shocked with his topic. Paul's wife exclaimed, "But you probably don't know, he's only had it twice and made him sick both times."

52. Real Airline humor:
"Folks, we have reached our cruising altitude now, so I am going to switch the seat belt sign off. Feel free to move about as you wish, but please stay inside the plane until we land...it's a bit cold outside, and walking on the wings affects the flight pattern."
As the plane landed and was coming to a stop at Washington National, a lone voice comes over the loudspeaker, "Whoa, big fella...WHOA!"
"Should the cabin lose pressure, oxygen masks will drop from the overhead area. Please place the bag over your own mouth and nose before assisting children or adults acting like children."
"As you exit the plane, please make sure to gather all your belongings. Anything left will be distributed evenly among the flight attendants. Please do not leave children or spouses."
"This plane is equipped with a video surveillance system. Any passenger not remaining in his/her seat until the plane comes to a complete stop will be strip searched at the terminal."

55.   A man boarded a plane in Miami destined for Dallas. After the plane took off, he went up to the cockpit. There he surprised the pilots by pulling a gun and demanding that the plane be taken to Dallas. Amazed, the pilot told the man that the plane was already going to Dallas to which the man answered, "Good, the last time I made this trip we were taken to Cuba!"

56.   An airline came out with the first fully automated plane. After all the passengers were on board, the plane started to taxi down the runway and a voice came over the intercom: "Welcome to the world's first automated plane. Since there is no way for human interference of the controls, there is absolutely no chance that anything can go wrong, anything can go wrong, anything can go wrong......"

57. Humorous air line crews:
"There may be 50 ways to leave your lover, but there are only 4 ways out of this airplane."
"Your seat cushions can be used for flotation, and in the event of an emergency water landing, please take them with our compliments."
"We do feature a smoking section on this flight; if you must smoke, contact a member of the flight crew and we will escort you to the wing of the airplane."
"Smoking in the lavatories is prohibited. Any person caught smoking in the lavatories will be asked to leave the plane immediately."
"Good morning. As we leave Dallas, it's warm, the sun is shining, and the birds are singing. We are going to Charlotte where it's dark, windy and raining. Why in the world y'all wanna go there, I really don't know."
And after landing: "Thank you for flying Delta Business Express. We hope you enjoyed giving us the business as much as we enjoyed taking you for a ride."

58. Subject: Communication!
This is from relatives and friends in Europe and the Mid East:

Let's face it -- English is a crazy language. There is no egg in egg-plant nor ham in hamburger; neither apple or pine in pineapple. English muffins weren't invented in England nor French fries in France. Sweetmeats are candies while sweetbreads, which aren't sweet, are meat.

We take English for granted. But if we explore its para-doxes, we find that quicksand can work slowly, boxing rings are square and a guinea pig is neither from Guinea nor is it a pig.

And why is it that writers write but fingers don't fing, gro-cers don't groce and hammers don't ham? If the plural of tooth is teeth, why isn't the plural of booth beeth? One goose, 2 geese. So one moose, 2 meese? One index, 2 indices?

Doesn't it seem crazy that you can make amends but not one amend, that you comb through annals of history but not a sin-gle annal? If you have a bunch of odds and ends and get rid of all but one of them, what do you call it?

If teachers taught, why didn't preacher praught? If a vege-tarian eats vegetables, what does a humanitarian eat? If you wrote a letter, perhaps you bote your tongue?

Sometimes I think all the English speakers should be com-mitted to an asylum for the verbally insane. In what language do people recite at a play and play at a recital? Ship by truck and send cargo by ship? Have noses that run and feet that smell? Park on driveways and drive on parkways? How can a slim chance and a fat chance be the same, while a wise man and wise guy are oppo-sites? How can overlook and oversee be opposites, while quite a lot and quite a few are alike? How can the weather be hot as hell one day and cold as hell another.

Have you noticed that we talk about certain things only when they are absent? Have you ever seen a horseful carriage or a strapful gown? Met a sung hero or experienced requited love? Have you ever run into someone who was combobulated, gruntled, ruly or peccable? And where are all those people who ARE spring chick-ens or who would ACTUALLY hurt a fly?

You have to marvel at the unique lunacy of a language in which your house can burn up as it burns down, in which you fill in a form by filling it out and in which an alarm clock goes off by going on.

English was invented by people, not computers, and it reflects the creativity of the human race (which, of course, isn't a race at all). That is why, when the stars are out, they are visible, but when the lights are out, they are invisible. And why, when I wind up my watch, I start it, but when I wind up this essay, I end it.

60. The Proxy Father - The Smiths had no children and decided to use a proxy father to start their family. On the day the proxy father was to arrive, Mr. Smith kissed his wife and said, "I'm off. The man should be here soon". Half an hour later, just by chance, a door-to-door baby photographer rang the doorbell, hoping to make a sale. "Good morning madam. You don't know me but I've come to..." "Oh, no need to explain. I've been expecting you," Mrs. Smith cut in. "Really?" the photographer asked. "Well, good! I've made a specialty of babies."
"That's what my husband and I had hoped. Please come in and have a seat." "Just where do we start?" asked Mrs. Smith, blushing. "Leave everything to me. I usually try two in the bathtub, one on the couch and perhaps a couple on the bed. Sometimes the living room floor is fun too; you can really spread out."
"Bathtub, living room floor? No wonder it didn't work for Harry and me." "Well, madam, none of us can guarantee a good one every time. But if we try several different positions and I shoot from six or seven angles, I'm sure you'll be pleased with the results."
"I hope we can get this over with quickly," gasped Mrs. Smith.
"Madam, in my line of work, a man must take his time. I'd love to be in and out in five minutes, but you'd be disappointed with that, I'm sure."
"Don't I know !!", Mrs. Smith exclaimed.
The photographer opened his briefcase and pulled out a portfolio of his baby pictures. "This was done on the top of a bus in downtown

London."

"Oh my!!!", Mrs. Smith exclaimed, tugging at her handkerchief.

"And these twins turned out exceptionally well when you consider their mother was so difficult to work with." The photographer handed Mrs. Smith the picture.

"She was difficult?" asked Mrs. Smith.

"Yes, I'm afraid so. I finally had to take her to Hyde Park to get the job done right. People were crowding around four and five deep, pushing to get a good look."

"Four and five deep?" asked Mrs. Smith, eyes widened in amazement.

"Yes", the photographer said. "And for more than three hours too. The mother was constantly squealing and yelling. I could hardly concentrate.

Then darkness approached and I began to rush my shots. Finally, when the squirrels began nibbling on my equipment, I just packed it all in."

Mrs. Smith leaned forward. "You mean they actually chewed on your, eh...equipment?"

"That's right. Well madam, if you're ready, I'll set up my tripod so that we can get to work."

"Tripod??", Mrs. Smith looked extremely worried now.

"Oh yes, I have to use a tripod to rest my Canon on. It's much too big for me to hold while I'm getting ready for action.

Madam ? Madam?...Good Lord, she's fainted !!"

61. You might be a Yankee if...

The sound of Fran Drescher's voice doesn't bother you.

You've watched the movie "Deliverance" and you're afraid to go on a camping trip. Ever.

For breakfast, you'd rather have potatoes than grits.

You can name at least 4 hockey teams.

You don't know what a moon pie is.

You've never eaten Okra.

You wonder why people in restaurants don't talk as loud as you do.

You have never planned your summer vacation around a gun &

knife show.

You don't have any problems pronouncing "Worcestershire sauce" correctly.

You've never had grain alcohol.

You are familiar with all the rules to Lacrosse.

You have no idea what a polecat is.

You don't see anything wrong with putting a sweater on a poodle.

You've never had bangs.

You'd rather vacation at Martha's Vineyard than Six Flags.

You don't have at least one can of WD-40 somewhere around the house.

You would rather have your son become a lawyer than grow up to get his own TV fishing show.

You refer to two or more people as "you guys" instead of "y'all".

You think more money should go to important scientific research at your university than to pay the salary of the head football coach.

You prefer a bagel over a donut.

You don't know anyone with two first names (i.e. Joe Bob, Billy Bob, Kay Bob, Bob Bob)

You get freaked out when strangers in public talk to you.

None of your fur coats are made with real fur.

You don't know what a Piggly-Wiggly is.

You think NASCAR stands for the North American Society for... (something)

You eat fried chicken with a knife and fork.

Your idea of a perfect meal is "Lahbsta and Clam Chowdah."

You use the horn in your car more than once or twice a year.

Everything you know about the Civil War you learned watching TV.

You don't "reckon".

You're not "fixin" to do anything.

62.   For some people it is easy to brighten up a room. It happens every time they leave it!

63.   LAWYER JOKE!!!
The local United Way office realized that it had never received a donation from the town's most successful lawyer. The volunteer in charge of contributions called him to persuade him to contribute. "Our research shows that out of a yearly income of more than $600,000 you give not a penny to charity. Wouldn't you like to give back to the community in some way?"

The lawyer mulled this over for a moment and replied, "First, Did your research also show that my mother is dying after a long illness, and has medical bills that are several times her annual income?" Embarrassed, the United Way rep mumbled, "Um... No."
"Second, that my brother, a disabled veteran, is blind and confined to a wheelchair?" The stricken United Way rep began to stammer out an apology but was put off. "Third, that my sister's husband died in a traffic accident," the lawyer's voice rising in indignation, "Leaving her penniless with three children?"
The humiliated United Way rep, completely beaten, said simply, "I had no idea..." On a roll, the lawyer cut him off once again, "...And I don't give any money to them, so why should I give any to you?!"

64.   Having her hair done at a West Hempstead beauty parlor, a woman told a cautionary tale about racial prejudice. The story deserves a wider audience.
On a recent weekend in Atlantic City, the woman related, she won a bucketful of quarters at a slot machine. She took a break from the slot for dinner with her husband in the hotel dining room. But first she wanted to stash the quarters in her room. "I'll be right back and we'll go to eat," she told her husband and she carried the coin-laden bucket to the elevator bank.
As she was about to walk into an elevator she noticed two men already aboard. Both were black. One of them was big. Very big. An intimidating figure. The woman froze. Her first thought was: These two are going to rob me. Her next thought was: Don't be a bigot, they look like perfectly nice gentlemen, even if one of them is awfully black.   But racial stereotypes are powerful, and fear im-

mobilized her. She stood and stared at the two men. She felt anxious, flustered, and ashamed. She hoped they didn't read her mind but knew they surely did; her hesitation about joining them on the elevator was all too obvious.

Her face burned. She couldn't just stand there, so with a mighty effort of will she picked up one foot and stepped forward and followed with the other foot and was on the elevator. Avoiding eye contact, she turned around stiffly and faced the elevator doors as they closed. A second passed, and then another second, and then another. The elevator didn't move. Panic consumed her.

My God, she thought, I'm trapped and about to be robbed! Her heart plummeted. Perspiration poured from every pore. Then one of the men said, "Hit the floor." Instinct told her: Do what they tell you. The bucket of quarters flew upwards as she threw out her arms and collapsed on the elevator carpet. A shower of coins rained down on her.

Take my money and spare me, she prayed. More seconds passed. She heard one of the men say politely, "Ma'am, if you'll just tell us what floor you're going to, we'll push the button." The one who said it had a little trouble getting words out. He was trying to hold in a belly laugh. She lifted her head and looked up at the two men. They reached down to help her up.

Confused, she struggled to her feet. "When I told my man here to hit the floor," one of the men, the average sized one, told her, "I meant that he should hit the elevator button for our floor. I didn't mean for you to hit the floor, ma'am." He spoke genially. He bit his lip. It was obvious he was having a hard time not laughing.

She thought: My Goodness, what a spectacle I've made of myself. She was too humiliated to speak. She wanted to blurt out an apology, but words failed her.

How do you apologize to two perfectly respectable gentlemen for behaving as though they were robbing you? She didn't know. The three of them gathered up the strewn quarters and refilled her bucket.

When the elevator arrived at her floor they insisted on walking her to her room. She seemed a little unsteady on her feet, and they were afraid she might not make it down the corridor. At her door they bid her good evening. As she slipped into her room she could hear them laughing while they walked back to the elevator bank.

The woman brushed herself off. She pulled herself together and went downstairs for dinner with her husband. The next morning flowers were delivered to her room - a dozen roses. Attached to each rose was a crisp one dollar bill. A card said: "Thanks for the best laugh we've had in years." It was signed, Eddie Murphy and Bodyguard

65. 21 reasons you know you work in the U.S in the nineties when...

21. Cleaning up the dining area means getting the fast food bags out of the back seat of your car.

20. Your reason for not staying in touch with family is that they do not have email addresses.

19. Keeping up with sports entails adding ESPN's home page to your bookmarks.

18. You have a "to do list" that includes entries for lunch and bathroom breaks and they are usually the ones that never get crossed off.

17. You have actually faxed your Christmas list to your parents.

16. Pick up lines now include a reference to liquid assets and capital gains.

15. You consider 2nd day Air Delivery and Inner-office Mail painfully slow.

14. You assume any question about whether to valet park or not is rhetorical.

13. You refer to your dining room table as the flat filing cabinet.

12. Your idea of being organized is multiple colored post-it notes.

11. Your grocery list has been on your refrigerator so long some of the products don't even exist anymore.

10. You lecture the neighborhood kids selling lemonade on ways to improve their process.

9. You get all excited when it's Saturday so you can wear sweats to work.

8. You refer to the tomatoes grown in your garden as deliverables.

7. You find you really need PowerPoint to explain what you do for a living.

6. You normally eat out of vending machines and at the most expensive restaurant in town within the same week.

5. You think that "progressing an action plan" and "calendarizing a project" are acceptable English phrases.

4. You know the people at the airport hotels better than your next door neighbors.

3. You ask your friends to "think out of the box" when making Friday night plans.

2. You think Einstein would have been more effective had he put his ideas into a matrix.

And, the number one sign you work in the nineties in U.S...

1. You think a "half-day" means leaving at 5 o'clock.

66. 1. Did you hear about the guy that lost his left arm and leg in a car crash? He's all right now.

2. How do crazy people go through the forest? They take the psycho path.

3. How does a spoiled rich girl change a light bulb? She says, "Daddy, I want a new apartment."

4. What did the fish say when he hit a concrete wall? "Dam".

5. What do Eskimos get from sitting on the ice too long? Polaroids.

6. What do prisoners use to call each other? Cell phones.

7. What do the letters D.N.A. stand for? National Dyslexics Association.

8. What do you call a boomerang that doesn't come back? A stick.

9. What do you call cheese that isn't yours? Nacho Cheese.

10. What do you call Santa's helpers? Subordinate Clauses.

11. What do you call four bull fighters in quicksand? Quatro sinko.

12. What do you get from a pampered cow? Spoiled milk.

13. What do you get when you cross a snowman with a vampire? Frostbite.

14. What do you get when you cross an elephant and a skin doctor? A pachydermatologist

15. What has four legs, is big, green, fuzzy, and if it fell out of a tree would kill you?
A pool table.
16. What is a zebra? 26 sizes larger than an "A" bra.
17. What kind of coffee was served on the Titanic? Sanka.
18. What kind of lettuce was served on the Titanic? Iceberg.
19. What lies at the bottom of the ocean and twitches? A nervous wreck.
20. What's the difference between roast beef and pea soup? Anyone can roast beef.
21. Where do you find a no legged dog? Right where you left him.
22. Where does virgin wool come from? Ugly sheep.
23. Why are there so many Smiths in the phone book? They all have phones.
24. Why do bagpipers walk when they play? They're trying to get away from the noise.
25. Why do gorillas have big nostrils? Because they have big fingers.

67. More weird language
What's with the people who put carpeting on the lid of their toilet seat? What are they thinking -- "Gosh, if we have a party there may not be enough standing room; I'd better carpet the toilet too."

Have you ever noticed that the waiter who takes your order is not the one who brings your food anymore? What is THAT about? And which waiter are you tipping, anyway? I think next time I go to a restaurant I'll just say, "Oh, sorry, I only eat the food. The guy who pays the bill will be along soon.

Would somebody please explain to me those signs that say, "No animals allowed except for Seeing Eye Dogs?" Who is that sign for? Is it for the dog, or the blind person?

Can't we just get rid of wine lists? Do we really have to be reminded every time we go out to a nice restaurant that we have no idea what we are doing? Why don't they just give us a trigonometry quiz with the menu?

If airline seat cushions are such great flotation devices, why don't you ever see anyone take one to the beach?

Why do they call it a "building"? It looks like they're finished. Why isn't it a "built"?

Why is it when you turn on the TV you see ads for telephone companies, and when you turn on the radio you hear ads for TV shows, and when you get put on hold on the phone you hear a radio station?

Why is it illegal to park in a handicapped parking space but okay to go to the bathroom in a handicapped stall?

How come you have to pay someone to rotate your tires? Isn't that the basic idea behind the wheel? Don't they rotate on their own?

All the king's HORSES and all the king's men? Are you kidding me? No wonder they couldn't put Humpty together again. Just what did those idiots expect the horses to do, anyway?

Did you ever notice, when you are sitting at a red light, that when the person in front of you pulls up a couple of inches, you are compelled to move up too? Do we really think we are making progress toward our destination? "Whew, I thought we would be late, but now that I am nine inches closer, I can stop for coffee and a danish!"

Have you ever noticed how they keep improving your laundry detergent, but they still can't get those blue flakes out? Why do we trust them to get our clothes clean? These guys can't even get the DETERGENT white!

Did you see these new minivan ads? All they talk about are cup holders, kiddie seats and doors. What kind of advertising is that? When you see an ad for a suit, do they say, "And look at the zipper! Carefully hidden, but easily accessible when you need it!" I think not.

68.   Three men were talking in a pub. Two of them were talking about the amount of control they had over their wives. After a

while, one of the first two turned to the third and said, "Well, what about you? What sort of control do you have?" The third man said "I'll tell you. Just the other day my wife came to me on her hands and knees." "What happened?" his friends asked. "She said," the third man replied, "'Get out from under that bed and fight like a man!' "

69. A man is flying in a hot air balloon and realizes he is lost. He reduces height and spots a man down below. He lowers the balloon further and shouts: "Excuse me, can you tell me where I am?" The man below says: "Yes, you're in a hot air balloon, hovering 30 feet above this field."
"You must work in Information Technology" says the balloonist. "I do" replies the man. "How did you know?" "Well," says the balloonist, "everything you have told me is technically correct, but it's no use to anyone."
The man below says, "You must be in management." "I am," replies the balloonist, "but how did you know?" "Well," says the man, "you don't know where you are or where you're going, but you expect me to be able to help. You're in the same position you were before we met, but now it's my fault."

70. A pastor of one church who was previously a sailor, was very aware that ships are addressed as "she" and "her". He often wondered what gender computers should be addressed. To answer that question, he set up two groups of computer experts. The first was comprised of women, and the second of men.
Each group was asked to recommend whether computers should be referred to in the feminine gender, or the masculine gender. They were asked to give 4 reasons for their recommendation.
The group of women reported that the computers should be referred to in the masculine gender because:
1. In order to get their attention, you have to turn them on.
2. They have a lot of data, but are still clueless.
3. They are supposed to help you solve problems, but half the time they are the problem.

4. As soon as you commit to one, you realize that, if you had waited a little longer you could have had a better model.

The men, on the other hand concluded that Computers should be referred to in the feminine gender because:
1. No one but the Creator understands their internal logic.
2. The native language they use to communicate with other computers is incomprehensible to everyone else.
3. Even your smallest mistakes are stored in long-term memory for later retrieval.
4. As soon as you make a commitment to one, you find yourself spending half your paycheck on accessories for it.

71. A father came home from a long business trip to find his son riding a very fancy new 10 speed bike. "Where did you get the money for the bike? It must have cost $300." "Easy, Dad," the boy replied. "I earned it hiking." "Come on," the father said. "Tell me the truth." "That is the truth," the boy replied. "Every night you were gone, Mr. Reynolds from the grocery store would come over to see Mom. He'd give me a $20 bill and tell me to take a hike!"

72. Scientist revealed that beer contains a small trace of female hormones. To prove their theory, the scientists fed 100 males 12 cans of beer and observed the results. 100% of the men gained weight, talked excessively without making sense, became emotional and couldn't drive. No further testing is necessary.

73. Getting Old: First you forget names. Then you forget faces. Then you forget to pull your zipper up. Then you forget to pull your zipper down. I don't know how I got over the hill without getting to the top. The golden years are really the metallic years. Gold in the teeth, silver in the hair, and (most of all) lead in the pants.

74. A farmer and his brand new bride were riding home from the chapel in a wagon pulled by a team of horses, when the older horse

stumbled.   The farmer said, "That's once." A little further along, the poor old horse stumbled again. The farmer said, "That's twice." After a little, while the poor old horse stumbled again. The farmer didn't say anything, but reached under the seat, pulled out a shotgun and shot the horse. His brand new bride raised all kind of heck with him, telling him, "That was an awful thing to do." The farmer said, "That's once."

75.An out-of-towner drove his car into a ditch in a desolated area. Luckily, a local farmer came to help with his big strong horse named Buddy. He hitched Buddy up to the car and yelled, "Pull, Nellie, pull!" Buddy didn't move. Then the farmer hollered, "Pull, Buster, pull!" Buddy didn't respond. Once more the farmer commanded, "Pull, Coco, pull!"   Nothing. Then the farmer nonchalantly said, "Pull, Buddy, pull!" And the horse easily dragged the car out of the ditch. The motorist was most appreciative and very curious. He asked the farmer why he called his horse by the wrong name three times. The farmer said, "Oh, Buddy is blind and if he thought he was the only one pulling, he wouldn't even try!"

76. The length of a marriage is inversely proportional to the amount of money spent on the wedding.

77. In response to calls for sexual equity, Pillsbury recently added a new Pillsbury Doughgirl character to the well known Doughboy. Unfortunately, she couldn't come to work this week because she had a yeast infection.

78. An eighty year old man was having an annual physical. As the doctor was listening to his heart with the stethoscope, he began muttering, "Oh oh !"   The man asked the doctor what the problem was.
"Well," said the Doc, "you have a serious heart murmur. Do you smoke ?" "No", replied the man.
"Do you drink in excess? "No." replied the man. "Do you have a sex life?" "Yes, I do!"
"Well," said the Doc, "I'm afraid with this heart murmur, you'll

have to give up half your sex life "
Looking perplexed, the old man said, "Which half...the LOOKING
or the THINKING???"

79.   A fellow stopped at a rural gas station and, after filling his
tank, he paid the bill and bought a soft drink. As he stood by his
car, drinking his Coke, he noticed a couple of men working along
the roadside. One man would dig a hole two or three feet deep and
then move on. The other man came along behind and filled in the
hole. While one was digging a new hole, the other was about 25
feet behind filling in the old.

The men worked right past the fellow with the Coke and
went on down the road. "I can't stand this," said the man, heading
down the road toward the men. "Hold it, hold it," he said to the
men. "Can you tell me what's going on here with this digging?"
"Well, we work for the county," one of the men said. "But one of
you is digging a hole and the other fills it up. You're not accom-
plishing anything. Aren't you wasting the county's money?"
"You don't understand, mister," one of the men said, leaning on his
shovel and wiping his brow. "Normally there's three of us -- me,
Rodney and Mike. I dig the hole, Rodney sticks in the tree and
Mike here puts the dirt back. Now just because Rodney's sick, that
don't mean that Mike and me can't work."

80.   We surveyed top personnel executives of 100 major American
corporations and asked for stories of unusual behavior by job ap-
plicants.   The lowlights:
1."... stretched out on the floor to fill out the job application."
2."She wore a Walkman and said she could listen to me and the
music at the same time."
3." A balding candidate abruptly excused himself. Returned to
office a few minutes later, wearing a hairpiece."
4."... asked to see interviewer's resume to see if the personnel executive was qualified to judge the candidate."
5."... announced she hadn't had lunch and proceeded to eat a hamburger and French fries in the interviewer's office - wiping the

ketchup on her sleeve."

6."Stated that, if he were hired, he would demonstrate his loyalty by having the corporate logo tattooed on his forearm."

7."Interrupted to phone his therapist for advice on answering specific interview questions."

8."When I asked him about his hobbies, he stood up and started tap dancing around my office."

9."At the end of the interview, while I stood there dumb struck, went through my purse, took out a brush, brushed his hair, and left."

10."... pulled out a Polaroid camera and snapped a flash picture of me. Said he collected photos of everyone who interviewed him."

11."Said he wasn't interested because the position paid too much."

12."While I was on a long-distance phone call, the applicant took out a copy of Penthouse, and looked through the photos only, stopping longest at the centerfold."

13."During the interview, an alarm clock went off from the candidate's brief case. He took it out, shut it off, apologized and said he had to leave for another interview."

14."A telephone call came in for the job applicant. It was from his wife. His side of the conversation went like this: "Which company? When do I start? What's the salary?" I said, "I assume you're not interested in conducting the interview any further." He promptly responded, "I am as long as you'll pay me more." [Interviewer] ``I didn't hire him, but later found out there was no other job offer. It was a scam to get a higher offer."

15."His attache [case] opened when he picked it up and the contents spilled, revealing ladies' undergarments and assorted makeup and perfume."

16."Candidate said he really didn't want to get a job, but the unemployment office needed proof that he was looking for one."

17."... asked who the lovely babe was, pointing to the picture on my desk. When I said it was my wife, he asked if she was home now and wanted my phone number. I called security."

18."Pointing to a black case he carried into my office, he said that if he was not hired, the bomb would go off. Disbelieving, I began to state why he would never be hired and that I was going to call the police. He then reached down to the case, flipped a switch and ran. No one was injured, but I did need to get a new desk."

81. The Year's Best Actual Headlines
1. Include Your Children When Baking Cookies
2. Something Went Wrong In Jet Crash, Expert Says
3. Police Begin Campaign To Run Down Jaywalkers
4. Safety Experts Say School Bus Passengers Should Be Belted
5. Drunk Gets Nine Months In Violin Case
6. Survivor Of Siamese Twins Joins Parents
7. Iraqi Head Seeks Arms
8. Prostitutes Appeal To Pope
9. Panda Mating Fails; Veterinarian Takes Over
10. British Left Waffles On Falkland Islands
11. Lung Cancer In Women Mushrooms
12. Eye Drops Off Shelf
13. Teachers Strike Idle Kids
14. Clinton Wins On Budget, But More Lies Ahead
15. Enraged Cow Injures Farmer With Ax
16. Plane Too Close To Ground, Crash Probe Told
17. Miners Refuse To Work After Death
18. Juvenile Court To Try Shooting Defendant
19. Stolen Painting Found By Tree
20. Two Sisters Reunited After 18 Years In Checkout Counter
21. Killer Sentenced To Die For Second Time In 10 Years
22. Never Withhold Herpes Infection From Loved One
23. War Dims Hope For Peace
24. If Strike Isn't Settled Quickly, It May Last A While
25. Cold Wave Linked To Temperatures
26. Deer Kill 17,000
27. Enfields Couple Slain, Police Suspect Homicide
28. Red Tape Holds Up New Bridge
29. Typhoon Rips Through Cemetery; Hundreds Dead
30. Man Struck By Lightening Faces Battery Charge
31. New Study Of Obesity Looks For Larger Test Group

32. Astronaut Takes Blame For Gas In Spacecraft
33. Kids Make Nutritious Snacks
34. Chef Throws His Heart In Helping Feed Needy
35. Arson Suspect Held In Massachusetts Fire
36. Ban On Soliciting Dead In Trotwood
37. Local High School Dropout Cuts In Half
38. New Vaccine May Contain Rabies
39. Hospitals Are Sued By 7 Foot Doctors
82. An elementary teacher told me one of her students was exclaiming he had a new baby brother. Then he added, "Mommy's not going to have any more babies cause she had her boobs tied."
83. Some people only get exercise when they let their imaginations run wild. Then they jump to conclusions

84. Farmer Joe decided his injuries from the accident were serious enough to take the trucking company responsible for the accident to court. In court the trucking company's fancy lawyer was questioning farmer Joe. "Didn't you say at the scene of the accident, 'I'm fine,'" asked the lawyer. Farmer Joe responded, "Well, I'll tell you what happened. I had just loaded my favorite mule Bessie into the..."

"I didn't ask for any details," the lawyer interrupted, "just answer the question. Did you not say at the scene of the accident, 'I'm fine!'."

Farmer Joe said, "Well, I had just got Bessie into the trailer and I was driving down the road..."

The lawyer interrupted again and said, "Judge, I am trying to establish the fact that, at the scene of the accident, this man told the highway patrolman on the scene that he was fine. Now several weeks after the accident he is trying to sue my client. I believe he is a fraud. Please tell him to simply answer the question."

By this time the judge was fairly interested in Farmer Joe's answer and said to the lawyer, "I'd like to hear what he has to say."

Joe thanked the Judge and proceeded, "Well, as I was saying, I had just loaded Bessie into the trailer and was driving her down the highway when this huge semi-truck and trailer ran the stop sign and smacked my truck right in the side.

I was thrown into one ditch and Bessie was thrown into the other. I was hurting real bad and didn't want to move. However, I could hear ol' Bessie moaning and groaning. I knew she was in terrible shape just by her groans. Shortly after the accident a highway patrolman came on the scene. He could hear Bessie moaning and groaning so he went over to her. After he looked at her, he took out his gun and shot her between the eyes. Then the Patrolman came across the road with his gun in his hand and looked at me." He said, "Your mule was in such bad shape I had to shoot her. How are you feeling?"

85. Holidays Christmas Carols for the Psychiatrically Challenged
SCHIZOPHRENIA - Do You Hear What I Hear?
MULTIPLE PERSONALITY - We Three Queens Disoriented Are.
DEMENTIA - I Think I'll Be Home For Christmas.
NARCISSISTIC -Hark The Herald Angels Sing (About Me)
MANIA - Deck the Halls and Walls and House and Lawn and Streets and Stores and Office and Town ...or Deck the Halls and spare No Expense!
PARANOIA - Santa Claus is Coming To Get Me.
PERSONALITY DISORDER - You Better Watch Out, I'm Gonna cry, I'm Gonna Pout, then MAYBE I'll tell you why.
DEPRESSION - Silent anhedonia, Holy anhedonia. All is calm, All is pretty lonely.
SERIAL KILLER - Slay Ride.
OBSESSIVE COMPULSIVE - Jingle Bell, Jingle Bell, Jingle Bell Rock, Jingle Bell, Jingle Bell, Jingle Bell Rock, Jingle Bell, Jin-gleBell, Jingle Bell Rock, Jingle Bell, Jingle Bell, Jingle Bell Rock, JingleBell, Jingle Bell, Jingle Bell Rock, Jingle Bell, Jingle Bell, Jingle Bell Rock, Jingle Bell, Jingle Bell, Jingle Bell Rock, Jingle Bell, Jingle Bell, Jingle Bell Rock, Jingle Bell...
BORDERLINE PERSONALITY - Thoughts of Roasting in an Open Fire.

PASSIVE AGGRESSIVE - On the First Day of Christmas My True Love Gave to Me (and then took it all away).
PSYCHOTIC - (actual lyrics) "here's the Story... of a man named Brady..."

86. "The Month After Christmas"
Twas the month after Christmas, and all through the house
Nothing would fit me, not even a blouse.
The cookies I'd nibbled, the eggnog I'd taste
At the holiday parties had gone to my waist.
When I got on the scales there arose such a number!
When I walked to the store (less a walk than a lumber).
I'd remember the marvelous meals I'd prepared;
The gravies and sauces and beef nicely rared,
The wine and the rum balls, the bread and the cheese
And the way I'd never said, "No thank you, please."
As I dressed myself in my husband's old shirt
And prepared once again to do battle with dirt---
I said to myself, as I only can
"You can't spend a winter disguised as a man!"
So--away with the last of the sour cream dip,
Get rid of the fruit cake, every cracker and chip
Every last bit of food that I like must be banished
Till all the additional ounces have vanished.
I won't have a cookie--not even a lick.
I'll want only to chew on a long celery stick.
I won't have hot biscuits, or corn bread, or pie,
I'll munch on a carrot and quietly cry.
I'm hungry, I'm lonesome, and life is a bore--
But isn't that what January is for?
Unable to giggle, no longer a riot.
Happy New Year to all and to all a good diet!

87. The old man went to the doctor with a ear ache. During the examination the doctor dislodged a suppository from the man's ear. Upon seeing it, the man called his wife. He said, "You can forget

looking for that hearing aide. I think I know where it is."

88. A young man was in a restaurant when a woman at a near-by table became choked. When he realized no one else was going to assist her, he ran to her table. He jerked her up on her feet, threw her skirt over her head, and took a big lick up her backside. The woman sputtered, coughed, and spit out the food lodged in her throat and began breathing. People came up to him congratulating him on his quick thinking. Someone asked, "How did you know what to do?" The man answered, "I haven't had any training, but I've been hearing an awful lot about that hinny-lick maneuver."

89. A new hair salon opened up across the street from an old established shop. They put up a huge sign "WE GIVE SEVEN DOLLAR HAIR CUTS." Not to be outdone, the shop across the street put up their own sign "WE FIX SEVEN DOLLAR HAIR CUTS."

90. A wealthy old farmer was having a family reunion. They all sat down to the table for a huge Sunday dinner. The old man looked around the table at his six healthy sons and their six healthy wives and said, "I have an announcement to make. I don't see any grandchildren around this table of mine. I want you all to know that I will give $10,000 to the first one of you who presents me with a grandchild. Now, please bow your heads for grace."
After a long prayer by the old man, he raised his eyes again. He and his wife were the only ones at the table.

91. Jake is struggling through an airport terminal with two huge and obviously heavy suitcases when a stranger walks up to him and asks: "Have you got the time?" Jake sighs, puts down the suitcases and glances at his wrist. "It's a quarter to six", he says.
"Hey, that's a pretty fancy watch!" exclaims the stranger.
Jake brightens a little. "Yeah, it's not bad. Check this out..." - and he shows him a time zone display not just for every time zone in the world, but for the 86 largest metropolis. He hits a few buttons and from somewhere on the watch a voice says "The time is eleven till

six" in a very West Texas accent. A few more buttons and the same voice says something in Japanese. Jake continues "I've put in regional accents for each city. The display is unbelievably high quality and the voice is simply astounding." The stranger is struck dumb with admiration.

"That's not all...", says Jake. He pushes a few more buttons and a tiny but very hi-resolution map of New York City appears on the display. "The flashing dot shows our location by satellite positioning", explains Jake. "View recede ten", Jake says, and the display changes to show eastern New York state.

"I want to buy this watch!" says the stranger.

"Oh, no, it's not ready for sale yet; I'm still working out the bugs", says the inventor. "But look at this", and he proceeds to demonstrate that "the watch is also a very incredible little FM radio receiver with a digital tuner, a sonar device that can measure distances up to 125 meters, a pager with thermal paper printout and, most impressive of all, the capacity for voice recordings of up to 300 standard-size books, though I only have 32 of my favorites in there so far" says Jake.

"I've got to have this watch!" says the stranger.

"No, you don't understand; it's not ready."

"I'll give you $1000 for it!"

"Oh, no, I've already spent more than ..."

"I'll give you $5000 for it!"

"But it's just not ..."

"I'll give you $15,000 for it!" And the stranger pulls out a checkbook.

Jake stops to think. He's only put about $8,500 into materials and development, and with $15,000 he can make another one and have it ready for merchandising in only six months. The stranger frantically finishes writing the check and waves it in front of him.

"Here it is, ready to hand to you right here and now. 15,000. Take it or leave it."

Jake abruptly makes his decision. "OK", he says, and peels off the watch and hands it to the stranger.

They make the exchange and the stranger starts happily away.

"Hey, wait a minute", calls Jake after the stranger, who turns around warily. Jake points to the two suitcases he had been trying to wrestle through the terminal. "Don't forget your batteries."

92. FUNNY SAYINGS

1. Everyone has a photographic memory. Some don't have film.
2. He who laughs last, thinks slowest.
3. A day without sunshine is like, well, night.
4. On the other hand, you have different fingers.
5. Change is inevitable, except from a vending machine.
6. Back up my hard drive?   How do I put it in reverse?
7. I just got lost in thought. It was unfamiliar territory.
8. When the chips are down, the buffalo is empty.
9. Seen it all, done it all, can't remember most of it.
10. Those who live by the sword get shot by those who don't.
11. I feel like I'm diagonally parked in a parallel universe.
12. He's not dead, he's electroencephalographically challenged.
13. She's always late. Her ancestors arrived on the Juneflower.
14. You have the right to remain silent. Anything you say will be misquoted, then used against you.
15. I wonder how much deeper the ocean would be without sponges.
16. Honk if you love peace and quiet.
17. Pardon my driving, I am reloading.
18. Despite the cost of living, have you noticed how it remains so popular?
19. Nothing is fool-proof to a sufficiently talented fool.
20. Don't worry about the world ending today, it's already tomorrow in Australia.
21. A loser is a window washer on the 44th floor who steps back to admire his work.
22. A man usually feels better after a few winks, especially is she winks back.
23. There's a fine line between fishing and standing on the shore like an idiot.
24. Did you ever walk into a room and forget why you walked in? I

think that's how dogs spend their lives.

25. Thousands of years ago, cats were worshipped as gods. Cats have never forgotten this.

26. A baby first laughs at the age of four weeks. By that time his eyes focus well enough to see you clearly.

27. In marriage, the facts are interesting, but totally irrelevant.

28. There's always one more imbecile than you counted on.

29. Nobody will ever win the battle of the sexes. There's too much fraternizing with the enemy.

30. When the chips are down, the buffalo is empty.

31. Seen it all, done it all, can't remember much of it.

32. I feel like I am diagonally parked in a parallel universe.

33. Middle age is when you are too young to take up golf and too old to rush the tennis net.

34. Friends may come and go, but enemies accumulate

35. Atheism is a non-prophet organization.

36. There are two kinds of people, those that do the work and those that take the credit. Try to be in the first group; there's less competition there.

37. Just remember this, a practical nurse is one who marries a wealthy patient.

39. And in the famous words of Yogi Berra, "If you don't know where you're going, you'll end up somewhere else!"

39. To golfers. One of the easiest ways to meet new people is to pick up the wrong ball on the golf course.

40. Nothing is impossible for those who don't have to do it.

41. The two most common elements in the universe are hydrogen and stupidity.

42. Playing golf is like raising children. You keep thinking you'll do better next time.

43. "I'd move heaven and earth to break 100," said the golf addict as he desperately banged away in a sand trap. "Try heaven," advised his partner. "You've moved enough earth already."

93. This shouldn't be funny but it is so odd that it is.

The US Standard railroad gauge (distance between the rails) is 4 feet, 8.5 inches. That's an exceedingly odd number. Why was that gauge used? Because that's the way they built them in England, and the US railroads were built by English expatriates.

Why did the English people build them like that? Because the first rail lines were built by the same people who built the pre-railroad tramways, and that's the gauge they used. Why did "they" use that gauge then? Because the people who built the tramways used the same jigs and tools that they used for building wagons, which used that wheel spacing.

Okay! Why did the wagons use that odd wheel spacing? Well, if they tried to use any other spacing the wagons would break on some of the old, long distance roads, because that's the spacing of the old wheel ruts.

So who built these old rutted roads? The first long distance roads in Europe were built by Imperial Rome for the benefit of their legions. The roads have been used ever since. And the ruts? The initial ruts, which everyone else had to match for fear of destroying their wagons, were first made by Roman war chariots. Since the chariots were made for or by Imperial Rome they were all alike in the matter of wheel spacing.

Thus, we have the answer to the original questions. The United States standard railroad gauge of 4 feet, 8.5 inches derives from the original specification for an Imperial Roman army war chariot. Specs and Bureaucracies live forever.

So, the next time you are handed a specification and wonder what horse's rear came up with it, you may be exactly right. Because the Imperial Roman chariots were made to be just wide enough to accommodate the back-ends of two war horses.

94. The armies of Alexander the Great were greatly feared in their day, but there was one problem that they had that almost defeated them. Alexander could not get his people to staff meetings on time. He always held the meetings at 6:00 P. M. each day after the day's battle was done, but frequently his generals either forgot or let the time slip up on them and missed the 6:00 P. M.

staff meeting. This angered Alexander very much, to say the least! So he called in his research team and set up a project to develop a method of determining the time at 6:00 P. M. each day. There were no clocks in those days, at least none that could be carried around. The smallest was a giant water clock "Find a way for my staff to determine the hour of the day, or at least when it gets to be 6:00 P. M.," he said, "Cost is no object." A study was instituted and, with several brain-storming sessions, his staff came up with the following idea. In a land some distance away, there grew a bush whose berries contained a type of dye that changed color at 6:00 P. M. each evening. They found that by dyeing strips of cloth and issuing them to the generals, they could see when it was 6:00 P. M. by the color change, and could consistently get to the 6:00 P. M. meetings on time. Needless to say this pleased Alexander very much. It was then turned over to his marketing group to come up with a name for this new invention as Alexander saw definite market potential in the strips. "It can be worn on the wrist and can be easily watched for the color change," said one junior executive. "I therefore propose to call it the Wrist Watch." This name was immediately discarded for being too bland and obvious. Another man suggested that since it could be worn in the naval and could be observed by just looking down, it should be called the Naval Observatory. This idea was rejected immediately as being too weird and too technical sounding for the general public. A junior Vice-President suggested that since it could be worn around the neck and would insure that you would be informed when it reached 6:00 P. M., it should be called the Six O'clock Noose, but this was rejected as too threatening.

Finally the senior vice president, who up to now had been silent, spoke and rendered his decision. "We shall call it a timeband, and in honor of the Great Alexander, it shall be known as ... 'Alexander's Rag Timeband!'

95. LAWS TO REMEMBER
THE LAW OF VOLUNTEERING - if you dance with a grizzly bear, you'd better let him lead.

THE LAW OF AVOIDING OVERKILL - when putting cheese in the mouse trap, always leave room for the mouse.

THE KNOW-WHEN-TO-QUIT LAW - the more you run over a dead animal, the flatter it gets.

THE FIRST LAW OF REALITY - there are some days when no matter which way you spit, it's upwind.

THE SECOND LAW OF REALITY - when you starve with a tiger, the tiger starves last.

THE THIRD LAW OF REALITY - whatever it is that hits the fan, it will not be evenly distributed.

THE FOURTH LAW OF REALITY - never get into fights with ugly people. They have nothing to lose.

THE FIFTH LAW OF REALITY - creativity is great but plagiarism is faster.

THE LAW OF GOAL SETTING - reality is a crutch for those that can't cope with fantasy.

96 . An older couple had been reading about the new miracle drug Viagra. After discussing this new drug, they decided to try it. The husband went to see the doctor who determined that Viagra was not the perfect medicine for him. Instead, the doctor offered him a different product that would have the same effect. The only problem with the new product was that it was a one-time shot and could only be given once, never again.
"After I give you this shot, you activate it by saying '1,2,3'" the doctor advised the husband. "To discontinue the effect, say '1,2,3,4.'" After receiving the shot of medication, the man went home to his wife. After a romantic candlelight dinner, they retired early for the night. After they got into bed, the husband carefully repeated "1,2,3," just like the doctor had directed him. His wife, unaware of the instructions, immediately responded, "What's the 1,2,3 for?"

97. An Amish gentleman and his son decide to visit the city mall. One of the most amazing things they ever had seen was a small room built off the main walkway with two silver doors on it. People would walk up to the closed doors, press a button, the doors would open and they would enter.

After seeing this from a distance, they decide to get a closer look. They watch as a somewhat unattractive woman presses the button and enters the room. After a few minutes, the doors open and a beautiful woman steps out into the mall. Without any hesitation, the father turns to his son and says, "Go get your mother."

98. Sven was going for his morning walk one day when he walked past Ole's house and saw a sign that said "Boat for Sale." This confused Sven because he knew that Ole didn't own a boat, so he finally decided to go in and ask Ole about it.

"Hey, Ole," said Sven, "I noticed da sign in your yard dat says 'Boat for Sale', but ya don't even have a boat. All ya have is your ol' John Deere tractor and combine." Ole replied, "Yep, and dey boat for sale."

99. One night Ole and his wife Lena were in bed when the phone rang. Ole answered it and Lena heard him yell, "Vell, how do heck should I know, dats over 2,000 miles away" and he hung up. Lena said, "Who was dat Ole?" Ole said "Heck, if I know, some wierdo want to know if da coast is clear."

100. IN PRISON...You spend the majority of your time in an 8x10 cell.
 AT WORK...You spend most of your time in a 6x8 cubicle.
IN PRISON...You get three meals a day.
 AT WORK...You only get a break for 1 meal and you have to pay for it.
 IN PRISON...You get time off for good behavior.
 AT WORK...You get rewarded for good behavior with more work.
 IN PRISON...A guard locks and unlocks all the doors for you.
 AT WORK...You must carry around a security card and unlock and open all the doors yourself.
 IN PRISON...You can watch TV and play games.
 AT WORK...You get fired for watching TV and playing games.
 IN PRISON...You get your own toilet.

AT WORK...You have to share.

IN PRISON...They allow your family and friends to visit.

AT WORK...You cannot even speak to your family and friends.

IN PRISON...All expenses are paid by taxpayers with no work required.

AT WORK...You get to pay all the expenses to go to work and then they deduct taxes from your salary to pay for prisoners.

IN PRISON...You spend most of your life looking through bars from the inside wanting to get out.

AT WORK...You spend most of your time wanting to get out and go inside bars.

IN PRISON...There are wardens who are often sadistic.

AT WORK...They are called supervisors.

IN PRISON...You have unlimited time to read e-mail jokes.

AT WORK...You get fired if you get caught.

101. Some real courtroom records:

Q. What is your date of birth?

A.. July fifteenth.

Q. What year?

A. Every year.

Q. What gear were you in at the moment of the impact?

A. Gucci sweats and Reeboks.

Q. This myasthenia gravis - does it affect your memory at all?

A. Yes.

Q. And in what ways does it affect your memory?

A. I forget.

Q. You forget. Can you give us an example of something that you've forgotten?

Q. All your responses must be oral, OK? What school did you go to?

A. Oral

Q. How old is your son - the one living with you?

A. Thirty-eight or thirty-five. I can't remember which.

Q. Who long has he lived with you?
A. Forty-five years.

102. A modern day up-date to a Father-Son discussion:
"George Washington, did YOU chop down the cherry tree?"
"No, Dad."
"I think you are lying."
"No, no, no! I swear I did NOT chop down the cherry tree."
"Son, I saw you out here with your ax. Your punishment will be much worse for you if you lie. Now, tell me the truth!"
"I did tell you the truth. Honest."
(seven months later...) "Dad, I answered your question truthfully. Still, I must take complete responsibility for all my actions. While my answer was legally accurate, I did not volunteer information. "Indeed, Dad, I did cause the cherry tree to be lying on the ground. To do this was wrong. It constituted a critical lapse in judgment and a personal failure on my part for which I am solely and completely responsible. "I know my answer to you gave a false impression. I misled you, my own father. I deeply regret that. "I can only tell you I was motivated by many factors. First, by a desire to protect myself from the embarrassment of my own conduct. "I was also very concerned about protecting Mom from this shock. "What I did, Dad, was use a SAW to cause the cherry tree to fall. Only after the tree was already down did I go get my ax to chop off individual branches. So, I chopped off branches, but sawed down the tree. Look at the saw cut on the stump and the ax cuts on the branches. Therefore, legally, I told the truth. "I ask you to turn away from the spectacle of this fallen tree and to return our attention to a solid family relationship."

103. There was this lady that was known all her life as being cheap. Everyone in the town called her cheap. Whenever she went shopping, an item had to be on sale or she just wouldn't buy it. She even washed her paper plates.

One day her husband passed away. She mourned for a little while until she found out the cost of the funeral. She then began to get mad at her deceased husband for leaving her all the expense of the arrangements.

She reluctantly went into town to the local newspaper office to put a death notice in the paper. The first thing she said was "How much is this going to cost me?" The news clerk told her the rate was 25 cents a word. She then instructed him to put a notice in the paper which read "Harry Smith Died." The Clerk then said "I'm sorry Mrs. Smith, but you must have at least seven words." She thought for a minute and then said, "OK, put this...Harry Smith Died, Ford Pick-Up for sale."

104. PARTING JOKES: "Just to establish some parameters," said the professor to a student from Arkansas, "What is the opposite of joy?" "Sadness," said the student.
"And what's the opposite of depression?" he asked a student from Oklahoma. "Elation." "And sir" he asked a student from Texas, "What's the opposite of woe?" "Sir, I believe that would be giddy up."

105. "One nice thing about telling a clean joke is there's a good chance that no one has heard it before."

106. One day a student was talking with his old professor about how dating had changed over the years. So the young student asked this old man how he chose a girl he wanted to ask out on a date back in his school days.

The old man took his time thinking and then replied, "Well, I went to Catholic school, so I did things a little differently. Every week I would go to confession, and while I was there, I would watch the girls going in and out of the confessional. Whichever girls was in there the longest, that is the one I would ask out."

A place for you to write your favorite jokes.

A place for you to write your favorite jokes.

Section III

Thanks so much for purchasing this book, reading it, and using the information you obtained. If it has helped you in anyway, would you please let me know.

1. If you have been helped in any health related ways, write me and your story may be told or written about in a future speech or book.

2. If you use some jokes in speeches let us know your results.

3. If you get lots of laughs from the book still let me know.

ABOUT THE AUTHOR
CAROL DEAN SCHREINER

Some people think of humor as being an inborn trait. Carol Dean has given birth five times and say, "Believe me, birthing is not a laughing matter. A joyous occasion but not a laughing matter!"

Carol Dean says jokes were always abounding in her home. Her mother's family was known for their jokes and their funny stories. Sometimes it was probably the laughs that kept them sane. That is if there is a mother of five who can be identified as sane.

She has earned the title of Distinguished Toastmasters of Toastmasters International. She is one of the very few Toastmasters of Oklahoma to have presented two programs at the Toastmasters International Conventions, one in 1990 the other in 1998.

CD is president of CD Communications. She presents keynotes and workshops, conducts speaker's schools, humor workshops, retreats and fills pulpits.

CD speaks to corporations, association, schools, churches. She is the only person who has spoken for the Oklahoma Education Association's annual convention for eight years.

Carol Dean is a consultant/trainer/manager with Arbonne International, a herbal, botanical skin care and health related company.

Carol Dean assisted with forming a chapter of the National Speakers Association for Oklahoma and was even the first woman president of that Oklahoma Association. She is listed in the 1993 Edition of Oxford's Who's Who Elite Registry of Extraordinary People.

Carol Dean has presented programs across USA, Canada and has been guest lecturer on cruise ships. She has authored three books, and has written for magazines. Her presentations fit under the umbrella of recycling self-esteem to success. They cover ways to improve people's lives with usually humorous approach.

Carol Dean is the host for a radio talk-show, "Out to Lunch with Carol Dean."

CD is an inspiration to all who come in contact with her. She has a special way of making anyone and everyone around her feel comfortable and at ease. Her children and grandchildren are extremely special and dear to her heart. Just speaking of any one of them puts not just a twinkle but a spot light in her eyes.

Her particular kind of humor and down-home warmth has had her referred to as the "Erma Bombeck of Oklahoma."

She still tells stores to her six grandchildren. Her plans are to speak and write as long as she can speak and write.

You may write to her at:

PO Box 5223

Norman, OK 73070-5223